Survey in Basic Christianity

Author—O. J. Gibson
Contributing Writer, Editor—S. M. Kennedy
Artist—Robin Clark

Produced as a service to the Lord's people by Fairhaven Ministries,
an outreach of Fairhaven Bible Chapel, 401 MacArthur Boulevard, San Leandro,
California. Fairhaven is an independent, autonomous, New Testament church
dedicated to evangelism and discipleship through the matrix of local churches
(Matthew 28:19-20; Acts 2:42).

D1441588

ECS
MINISTRIES
The Word to the World

ECS Ministries exists to glorify God by providing biblically-sound resources and structured study materials for the purpose of teaching people from every nation to know Jesus Christ as Savior and to live in a way that is consistent with God's Word.

Survey in Basic Christianity

O. J. Gibson

Published by:

    ECS Ministries

    PO Box 1028

    Dubuque, IA 52004-1028

    phone: (563) 585-2070

    email: ecsorders@ecsministries.org

    website: www.ecsministries.org

Reprinted 2009, 2014, 2016

ISBN 978-1-59387-096-6

Code: W-SBC

Many ECS Publications are also available in eBook formats. For more information, visit the ECS website www.ecsministries.org.

Printed in the United States of America

INTRODUCTION

This workbook is designed to be used in a class or small group. The instructions below suggest the best way to use the material. The study can also be used by an individual in their personal study.

Instructions

The following suggestions will make this study profitable.

1. Pray to God.

Ask God to help you understand His Word. Claim the promise of Psalm 119:130: "The entrance of thy Words giveth light, it giveth understanding unto the simple." It is impossible to truly understand God's Word without God's help (1 Corinthians 2:14).

2. Prepare Before Class.

a. Read the Notes. Read and reread the lesson. Underline key thoughts, mark anything that you do not understand or that you have questions about. Make notations on the wide margin at the side of each lesson.

b. Look Up Key References. If time permits, read all Scripture references from a modern translation such as New American Standard Bible. A typical reference is written with the name of the book followed by the chapter number and verse number which are separated by a colon (example: Colossians 3:23). The abbreviation "cf." means to compare two references (example: Psalm 45:6-7, cf. Hebrews 1:8). Most Bibles have a table of contents that lists the starting page number for each book of the Bible. After finding the page, locate the appropriate chapter and verse.

c. Answer Homework Questions. Complete all items of the homework as directed. If you have trouble with a question, pass on to the next question.

3. Attend Class Regularly.

There is a time for small group interaction as well as a lecture period. Your questions and comments will encourage others to share.

4. Save Your Notes and Materials.

These will help you in your further study and you may wish to share them with others.

Table of Contents

Section/Title/Description   Page

"EVERYONE THAT IS OF THE TRUTH HEARETH MY VOICE," said the Lord Jesus before the Roman governor. "Pilate saith unto Him, What is truth?" (John 18:37-38). There is little value, in a lasting sense, of studying anything if we believe that (1) there is no such thing as truth, or (2) truth is always changing, or (3) it is impossible to know truth with any certainty.

Truth has been defined as: conforming to fact or reality; being in accord with what is, has been, or must be; it is the opposite of false, wrong, error or lie. Truth is narrow and unchanging, regardless of history and culture; it is absolute and independent of anything else. To believe otherwise is destructive to both learning and morals.

The Search for Truth

The Psalmist cried out, "Lead me in thy truth, and teach me" (Psalm 25:5). He believed that this truth is forever (117:2). Because it is so precious, we are advised, "Buy the truth, and sell it not" (Proverbs 23:23). The prophet spoke of "the God of Truth" (Isaiah 65:16). The Lord Jesus said, "I am . . . the truth" (John 14:6) and "thy Word is truth" (John 17:17).

It would seem that all men would wish to "come unto the knowledge of the truth" (1 Timothy 2:4). Yet we are told that mankind generally has "exchanged the truth of God for a lie, and worshipped and served the creature rather than the Creator" (Romans 1:25 NASB). Those who say they are truth-seekers often do not love the truth (2 Thessalonians 2:10). They rather seek their own way, and that way is a path of error. But Jesus promised to true seekers, "Ye shall know the truth, and the truth shall make you free" (John 8:32). Men need to know the truth about God, about life, about eternity.

The Source of Truth

Where shall we seek the truth? Some seek it *within themselves*. They believe their own reason, emotions and desires are a sufficient guide. Some seek it *among themselves*. They look to the advice, experiences and teaching of other persons. Some seek it *beyond themselves*. They believe that truth is greater than our own limited ability as men to understand. It requires the help of God or a supernatural power.

The act of God in communicating certain things which we could not know otherwise is called *revelation*. The act of guiding men to write down a communication of the truth He wishes to reveal is called *inspiration*. The claim that God did exactly that, in giving us the 66 books of the Bible, is made by the prophets, the apostles and by Jesus Christ Himself.

It is called both the "Scripture" and the "Scriptures" (Mark 12:10; 12:24), meaning that these are sacred writings. We call these collected writings the Bible, meaning "the Book"—signifying its place above all other books. These writings are further called "the Word of God" (Mark 7:13; Romans 10:17; 2 Corinthians 2:17; 1 Thessalonians 2:13; Hebrews 4:12).

Such expressions as "God said," "the Lord spoke" and "the Word of the Lord came" occur perhaps 3,000 times in the Old Testament alone. God is represented as speaking directly on many occasions (Exodus 24:12; Deuteronomy 10:1-2). The writers of Scripture said that God was giving His words through them to men. Consider these statements by holy men of God:

Moses: "And God said"; "the Lord said" (Exodus 3:14-15; Deuteronomy 1:42)
Joshua: "The Lord spake" (Joshua 1:1)
Jeremiah: "The Lord said"; "saith the Lord" (Jeremiah 1:7-9)
Ezekiel: "He said unto me" (Ezekiel 3:4)
Malachi: "Thus saith the Lord" (25 times)
Jesus: "All [will] be fulfilled" (Matthew 5:18, speaking of the Old Testament Law)
    "The commandment of God" (Mark 7:8, speaking of the Old Testament Law)
    "It is written" (John 6:45, speaking of the Old Testament Prophets)
    "They have Moses and the Prophets" (Luke 16:29-31)
    "Written in the law . . . the prophets . . . the psalms" (Luke 24:44)
The Apostles: "Holy Spirit foretold" (Acts 1:16 NASB)
    "The Holy Spirit rightly spoke" (Acts 28:25 NASB)

Comprehensive statements are made. "All Scripture is God-breathed" (2 Timothy 3:16 NASB, marginal reading). "Holy men of God spake as they were moved by the Holy Ghost" (2 Peter 1:21). "Not in the words which man's wisdom teacheth, but which the Holy Ghost teacheth" (1 Corinthians 2:13).

The Sign of Truth

The following considerations give evidence that the preceding statements are true:

1. Those who claimed to be inspired were of the highest moral and spiritual character. Who would accuse Moses, Paul, Isaiah, or even the Lord Jesus of being men of questionable character?

2. The Bible has a profound unity of teaching in spite of having been written by over 40 different men over a period of 1500 years. How else could we account for this unity?

3. The multitude of historical statements in the Scriptures have spurred volumes on archaeological confirmation of its truth. There is extensive support for statements dealing with historic events and persons.

4. The book has endured in its publication, distribution and world impact as the most important volume ever written. Yet it has been more extensively attacked than any other book, surviving many efforts to destroy every copy. What other book has sustained such criticism while continuing to be a best seller year after year?

5. It continues to have a transforming power in changing lives even today. Violent criminals as well as gentle people are touched and changed by its message. Millions have been given hope, comfort and encouragement in their darkest hours. What other book has changed so many lives for the better?

6. Detailed prophecies have been fulfilled by the hundreds. Where else do we find a prophetic record with one hundred per cent accuracy in every detail?

Great issues of life and eternity have challenged the minds of great men. They are defined and explained in Scripture. These lessons are designed to help the reader understand exactly what the Bible teaches on the subjects of God, man, sin, salvation, eternity and Jesus Christ. It is important to learn what the Bible really says before we decide whether we agree or disagree. Jesus said the errors of even the religious leaders of His day were due to the fact that they did not know the Scriptures (Matthew 22:29). Daniel said that these were "the Scripture[s] of truth" (Daniel 10:21). Do you know the truth?

THY WORD IS TRUTH   **LESSON 1**

Man has a longing for knowledge and truth. Many sources available to him, however, are not reliable. The Bible claims to be God's truth revealed to man.

1. Which of the following statements most accurately describes the Biblical concept of truth? (select one)
    a. There is no such thing as truth.
    b. Truth is always changing.
    c. It is impossible to know truth with any certainty.
    d. Truth is absolute and knowable.

2. Prior to the birth of Christ, how did God communicate truth to man (Hebrews 1:1)?

    What built-in proof did God use to confirm that the prophets were speaking the truth (Deuteronomy 18:22)?

    What did the prophets indicate about the origin of their words?

3. What is God's ultimate means of communicating truth (Hebrews 1:2; Matthew 17:5)?

    What did Jesus say about truth (John 14:6; 17:17)?

4. How did Jesus affirm the authority of the writers of the Old Testament Scriptures (Luke 24:44)?

    What attitude did He take toward the following Old Testament events?

    Creation of Adam and Eve (Mark 10:6)

    Jonah and the fish (Matthew 12:39-40)

    Noah and the ark (Matthew 24:37-39)

5. Why is it inconsistent to say that we accept the teaching of Jesus, yet reject the teachings of other parts of the Bible, such as Genesis (John 5:46-47)?

6. The New Testament writers recorded the words and teaching of Jesus. What attitude did they have about the authority of what they wrote (1 Corinthians 11:23; 2 Peter 1:16-21)?

7. What was one of the greatest errors of the religious leaders of Jesus' day (Matthew 22:29)?

8. Paraphrase (rewrite in your own words) 2 Timothy 3:15-17.

What is one of the best reasons to study the Bible (John 5:39 NASB)?

9. *What do you say?* Place a circle around the letter of each statement that best reflects your feelings about the Bible:

a. I believe the Bible is God's Word to man, and although written by many different men over a period of many years, it is error-free in its original writing and is reliable and trustworthy both in historical fact and in doctrinal statement.

b. I believe that only the words of Jesus in the Bible are inspired.

c. I believe that many of the stories in the Bible, such as Adam and Eve, Noah and the Ark are not meant to be taken literally, but still have meaning for teaching.

d. I believe that the Bible contains many contradictions.

e. I believe that the Bible contains all I need to know about God, life and the hereafter.

f. I believe that the Bible has many good moral teachings but is not absolute truth.

g. The truth of the Bible is for every generation, every culture, every race.

10. *What do others say?* Contact at least three people this week and ask them the following questions. You may wish to say something like the following:

> "I'm involved in a Bible Survey here in (name city). Could you help me by sharing your opinion on three important questions? (1) If you were God, and wanted to communicate to man, how would you do it? (2) Furthermore, how would you convince man that this was really your communication? (3) If someone would prove to you that the Bible was really true, would you be willing to conform your life to its moral teachings? Thank you so much for your help. Would you like for me to mail/e-mail you a copy of the survey results? Thank you."

Record their names and addresses on the 3x5 cards provided by the class leader. Record the answers on the back, indicating if survey results are desired. Then return the cards next class meeting. Results of the survey will be tabulated by the class leader and mailed to each person indicating an interest.

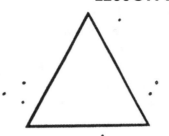

"I AM GOD, AND THERE IS NONE ELSE; I am God, and there is none like Me" (Isaiah 46:9). The Bible declares the voice of the one Supreme Being, "the high and lofty One that inhabiteth eternity" (Isaiah 57:15). Out of the mystery and infinity of His absolute being, He has declared Himself as "the living God" (Psalm 42:2; 84:2; Daniel 6:20; 1 Timothy 4:10; 6:17; Hebrews 9:14; 10:31).

"His greatness is unsearchable" (Psalm 145:3). His immensity is such that "in Him we live, and move, and have our being" (Acts 17:28). Again and again the cry has gone up, "O God, who is like unto thee?" (Psalm 71:19; cf. 89:8; 113:5). The reply must always come, "There is *none* like thee."

Popular Concepts About God

The name "God" has always been upon many lips. There have been those who have denied His existence, those who have used His name in cursing and those who have confused and misrepresented His being. Atheists say that there is no God and that they can prove it. Agnostics say it is impossible to know of His existence and they work diligently to lead millions in joining them in a declaration of ignorance. Pantheists say that God is merely nature, self-created, and that man is a part of it. Polytheists say there is not one God but many. Their ranks have included every variety from ancient pagans to modern day Mormons.

Other varied ideas have been put forward. It has been said that everything is God, including you and me, or that God is a principle, an impersonal law or force. It has been said that God is merely an idea in a person's mind, a psychological crutch or a neurosis (an irrational fear). Men have made images or idols that represent gods (Acts 19:23-28), although such a practice is forbidden in the Bible (Exodus 20:4-5). Many times men have called themselves gods and called on others to worship them. Some, who refuse to acknowledge any accountability to a Supreme Being, have in effect become their own gods.

Self-Evidence of God

The Bible does not attempt to prove there is a God. It assumes this knowledge is woven into the very being and consciousness of men. It says that the fool denies His existence (Psalm 14:1; 53:1). It notes that wicked men seek to forget Him (Psalm 10:4). In archaeology it is considered a proof that man has been present if there is evidence of the worship of God. No dictatorship has yet been able to wipe out the belief in God, in spite of strenuous efforts.

Man, throughout most of history, has been incurably convinced in the center of his being that God exists and that he is answerable to Him. This knowledge is the very basis of his accountability. "Because that which may be known of God is manifest in them; for God hath showed it unto them. For the invisible things of Him from the creation of the world are clearly seen, being understood by the things that are made, even His eternal power and Godhead; so that they are without excuse" (Romans 1:19-20).

The firm conviction of the existence of God was present long before man assembled arguments for and against the belief. It takes a systematic attack by the state, by the educational process and by the popular media to weaken belief in God. It is also evident that as pride, intellectual arrogance, wickedness and social degeneration increase, so does questioning about God's existence. Some ask, "Why should we believe in God? We can account for everything on a natural or evolutionary basis." Those who feel they are more intelligent than believers in God should consider:

1. Nothing is Self-Originating.

No scientific work has ever demonstrated an endless chain coming from nothing. In fact, nothing ever comes out of nothing. The Bible says, "every house is builded by some man; but He that built all things is God" (Hebrews 3:4).

2. Elaborate Structures Require a Maker or Designer.

Any major part of a man, such as his brain or his eye, is more complicated than a data processing machine or a watch. Yet no one would believe the latter came into existence by chance.

Biblical View of God

1. There is One God

Both Old and New Testaments alike proclaim that there is only one God (Deuteronomy 6:4; Isaiah 45:5; 1 Timothy 2:5). Judaism and Islam agree with the Christian faith in this. Men often speak of other gods (1 Corinthians 8:5-6) and the Bible sometimes uses the word in an inferior sense (Exodus 7:1; Psalm 82:6), but there is only one true God.

2. God Exists in Three Persons

The one God is a plural rather than a simple unity. He is one in essence but revealed in Scripture as plural in distinctions of personality. One name for God in the Old Testament is *Elohim*, used about 2600 times. It is *plural* in form though at times used with a singular verb. Deuteronomy 6:4 is the classic Jewish affirmation that there is only one God. "The Lord our God is one Lord." This verse uses *Elohim*. We further note that God often speaks of Himself even in the Old Testament as "us" or "we" (Gen. 1:26, 3:22). No king of Israel speaks of himself in this way.

There are references which intimate a distinction between "God and God" (Psalm 45:6-7, cf. Hebrews 1:8, or "The Lord said to my Lord" Psalm 110:1, cf. Matthew 22:42-46). The fuller revelation of God as existing as

Father, Son and Holy Spirit is given to us in the New Testament. Each is plainly called God, even though the New Testament plainly affirms there is only one God.

    a. The Father is God. See 1 Thessalonians 1:1; 2 Peter 1:17.

    b. The Spirit is God. See Acts 5:3-4; 2 Corinthians 3:17.

    c. The Son is God. See 1 John 5:20; Titus 2:13; John 1:1, 14; 20:26-28; Acts 20:28; Romans 9:5; Colossians 2:8-9; 1 Timothy 3:16; Hebrews 1:8; Revelation 1:8, 17-18.

All divine attributes are attributed to each. The qualities of will, emotion and reason are attributed to each. Father, Son and Holy Spirit are distinct from one another and yet joined in divine association (1 Peter 1:2; Jude 20-21). Their names are joined in the baptismal formula (Matthew 28:19) and the Apostolic Benediction (2 Corinthians 13:14). They can be further identified in the baptism of Jesus (Matthew 3:16-17), and the Discourses in John (John 14:16-20; 15:26; 16:7-16). The *oneness* is also shown (John 14:9; 17:22).

They are called the persons of the Godhead although they differ from what we mean by "persons." They are not three different gods, nor a three-headed god. There is but one God in substance. The word "Trinity" is used as a convenience to describe the Godhead although it is not in the Bible. The same is true with the expression "Triune God." Since we have nothing to parallel God in this respect, we have no term in our language that fully expresses this truth. The Bible does not explain it. We should accept the direct statements of Scripture and leave it at that.

3. God is Spirit

See John 4:24. He may take the form of a man or be heard in a voice. He may manifest Himself in some natural occurrence such as thunder or lightning. Yet He is an invisible spirit being who is not bound by space, time and form.

4. God Has Personality

He is not a mere principle or idea. Such personal characteristics as knowledge (1 John 3:20), sensibility or emotions (Genesis 6:6) and will or decision-making (James 1:18) are attributed to Him. He manifests both love and anger. He remembers or chooses to forget. He makes decrees and announces the future. God is not a self-functioning machine. It is of the greatest comfort to the believer to know that *God is love* (1 John 4:8, 16). No principle or impersonal force would justify the statement of 1 Peter 5:7, "Casting all your care upon Him for He careth for you."

The word for "God" in our language is taken from "good." He is indeed good. He is also called the Lord, the Almighty, the Creator, the Savior, the Redeemer and many other names. The name Jehovah is taken from JHVH, a four letter word for the Divine Name in the Old Testament. It was never pronounced and its full spelling or pronunciation is guess work. No one can Scripturally say that any one word is the only name acceptable for God. It is essential that we know the God of the Bible, who is the One commanding us to know His Son Jesus Christ. He is the only way to God (John 14:6).

THE PERSON OF GOD

It is important to know in whom we believe. What is He like? Do you have false ideas about Him?

1. God is (select one)
   a. an idea.
   b. a force.
   c. a man.
   d. a spirit.

2. Which of the following most describes *your* concept of God?
   a. policeman
   b. manager
   c. your own father on earth
   d. a machine
   e. none of the above

3. How would you describe God to someone who had not ever heard of Him?

4. Does the Bible attempt to prove the existence of God, or does the Bible assume that God's existence is self-evident (Genesis 1:1)?

   How would a person know there is a God even if he did not have the Bible (Psalm 19:1-4; Romans 1:19-20)?

   Why do you believe God exists?

5. The Bible teaches that there is
   a. one God.
   b. there are three gods.
   c. there are many gods.
   d. we all worship the same god.

6. How does the Bible account for other "gods" that men worship (1 Corinthians 8:5-6)? Paraphrase (rewrite in your own words) this passage.

7. How would you explain to someone the following: The Father is God. The Son is God. The Spirit is God. There is only one God.

8. God is a spirit means:
   a. He cannot be known by us.
   b. He cannot be seen.
   c. He cannot reveal Himself visibly.
   d. He is not personal.

9. *What do you say?* Because God is a person, it is possible to have a personal relationship with Him. How would you describe your present relationship with Him?

10. *What do others say?* Contact at least three people this week and ask them the following questions. You may wish to say something like the following:

    "I'm involved in a Bible Survey here in (name city). Could you help me by sharing your opinion on three important questions? (1) How would you define God? (2) In your opinion, what is the greatest proof that God exists (or if person does not believe God exists, ask why)? (3) If you could ask God anything, what would you ask? Thank you so much for your help. Would you like for me to mail/e-mail you a copy of the survey results? Thank you."

    Record their names and addresses on the 3x5 cards provided by the class leader. Record the answers on the back, indicating if survey results are desired. Then return the cards next class meeting. Results of the survey will be tabulated by the class leader and mailed to each person indicating an interest.

"TO WHOM THEN WILL YE LIKEN GOD? Or what likeness will ye compare unto Him?" asked the prophet (Isaiah 40:18). The Bible indicates that He is not exactly like anything or anybody we know. It does use our language to describe Him in human terms. The fact that it speaks of the arm, eye, hand or mouth of the Lord does not mean that He has these organs any more than it means He resembles a fowl when it says, "He shall cover thee with His feathers" (Psalm 91:4).

If He could be completely comprehended, explained and analyzed by man, then He would exist at man's level. We should beware of rejecting facts about God just because we have no similar reference point or experience with which we can compare. A man asked Job, "Canst thou find out the Almighty unto perfection?" (Job 11:7). The answer is that we can know about God what He is pleased to reveal about Himself in Scripture and no more. Some concepts exceed the limits of our understanding.

Unique Attributes (Those Only God Possesses)

Certain statements are made in Scripture about the characteristics of God as He has chosen to reveal them to us. We call them "attributes." God is:

1. Self-Existent.
He has life in Himself (John 5:26). He comes from nothing prior. He already existed in the beginning (Genesis 1:1; John 1:1).

2. Eternal.
From "everlasting to everlasting" He is God (Psalm 90:2; cf. Habakkuk 1:12). "He who is" expresses the name of I AM (Exodus 3:14), the One who compasses past, present and future (Revelation 4:8).

3. Infinite.
This means "without bounds or limits." Nothing can contain God (1 Kings 8:27). Nothing can measure Him.

4. All-Powerful.
The Almighty has power and authority to do whatever He chooses (Job 42:2; Matthew 19:26). This is called "omnipotence."

5. All-Knowing.
He has unlimited knowledge, understanding and awareness (Psalm 147:4-5). Nothing can be added to this in any way and nothing can either surprise

or deceive Him (Hebrews 4:13; 1 John 3:20). This is called "omniscience." He knows the end from the beginning (Isaiah 46:10). It includes His fore-knowledge of all things (Acts 2:23).

6. All-Present.

He is unlimited as to place or time. He is everywhere at all times (Psalm 139:7-12). This is called "omnipresence." He is inescapable (Jeremiah 23:23-24; Amos 9:2).

7. Changeless.

He may change in actions or dealings but He never changes in His eternal character and purposes (Malachi 3:6; James 1:17). He is neither fickle nor unfaithful. This is called "immutability."

8. Self-Sufficient.

He needs absolutely nothing from any source because He has no deficiencies (Acts 17:24-25).

9. Sovereign.

He is ruler and controller over all and none can hinder Him. He works all things after the counsel of His own will (Ephesians 1:11; Isaiah 40:13-14). He has the unrestricted right as God to do whatever He pleases (Romans 9:15-18). He does not owe anything to anyone.

Relative Attributes (Those Man Can Share)

1. Love.

This is that sacrificial and self-giving expression which seeks the highest good for another. It is practical and beneficial. Because God loved us, He gave His Son to die for us (John 3:16). His love is not dependent on the loveliness or responsiveness of the object. In fact, God loves the hostile, the unappreciative and the sinful person, though hating the sin (1 John 4:10; Ephesians 2:4-5; Romans 5:8; Jeremiah 31:3). Compassion is closely allied with love. It involves inner sympathy or pity for others (Psalm 86:15; Matthew 9:36; 14:14).

2. Wrath.

His holy displeasure against all evil wherein men persist and will not repent (Colossians 3:5-7; Romans 2:4-6) is not a contradiction to His love but a different aspect of His character. Romans 1:18 shows us the object of his wrath: "against all ungodliness and unrighteousness."

3. Grace.

His undeserved and freely-bestowed favor toward others is not a debt in response to good works (Romans 4:4-5; 11:6). Grace offers salvation to mankind (Ephesians 2:8; Titus 2:11).

4. Mercy.

His active pity or compassion toward offenders or the needy, whereby relief is given, is similar to grace (Psalm 103:8). God is rich in mercy (Ephesians 2:4).

5. Holiness.

He is apart from all other beings and there is no evil or impurity in Him (Psalm 99:9; Isaiah 57:15). He is called "The Holy One." Heaven chants His holiness (Revelation 4:8; Isaiah 6:3). In the absolute sense, none is holy but God (Revelation 15:4; Hebrews 7:26). This quality necessitates the punishment of sin (Isaiah 59:2). We are called to be holy because He is holy (1 Peter 1:16).

6. Righteousness and Justice.

These spring from the same root word in the original language of the New Testament. This is impartiality or fairness in dealing with others. Nothing wrong can proceed from Him (Nehemiah 9:33; Psalm 145:17). He is the righteous Judge (2 Timothy 4:8) and He will unfailingly do that which is right (Genesis 18:25). His justice demands that sin's penalty be paid and His love provides the payment so that He can be both "just, and the justifier of him which believeth in Jesus" (Romans 3:26).

7. Truth.

With God there is no falsehood, no unfaithfulness, no lack of consistency with Himself (Numbers 23:19; 1 John 5:20). He is the truth (John 14:6). He is absolutely and totally faithful (2 Timothy 2:13; Revelation 19:11).

8. Patience.

His self-imposed restraint of actions that otherwise might properly be taken is a quality that is becoming to one who has great power. Endurance with longsuffering toward that which is displeasing is one aspect (Romans 9:22; Acts 13:18); persistence in seeking good is another (2 Peter 3:9).

9. Wisdom.

God has all-knowledge, but His application of that knowledge displays an infinite wisdom—a deep understanding coupled with sound judgment (Romans 11:33; Ephesians 3:10). "There is no searching of His understanding" (Isaiah 40:28). The all-wise God searches the hearts of all men (Romans 8:27; 16:27).

10. Goodness.

His kindness of heart is the very quality which should lead men to repentance (Romans 2:4). God is full of this kindness, good will or benevolence (Psalm 119:68; 145:9). Human difficulties or sorrows should never cause us to doubt His goodness.

11. Generosity.

God is the greatest of all givers, having shown this in the supreme gift of His Son (John 3:16). That is why He loves cheerful givers (2 Corinthians 9:7). God gives liberally (James 1:5). It is He who opens the windows of heaven to pour down blessings. His style is to give *full* measure, "that there shall not be room enough to receive it" (Malachi 3:10).

THE LIKENESS OF GOD   LESSON 3

God's ways are governed by His character and His attributes. The following questions should help us to understand Him better.

1. It is difficult for man to understand what God is like because (select one)
    a. man thinks God is like he is.
    b. God's ways are "higher" than man's ways.
    c. there is nothing or no one with whom to compare God.
    d. God is unknowable.
    e. all of the above.
    f. a through c above.

2. What relationship does God have to everything that exists (Acts 17:24-25)?

    What characteristics of God are described in the following verses that emphasize His total independence and self-sufficiency? (Explain in your own words.)

    John 5:26; 1:1; Genesis 1:1

    Exodus 3:14; Psalm 90:2; Revelation 4:8

    1 Kings 8:27

3. Read Psalm 139. List three characteristics about God indicated in this passage.

    a.

    b.

    c.

4. Paraphrase (rewrite in your own words) Romans 8:28.

    What comfort can a Christian get from this passage?

5. Which of the following is *not true* of God's love (select one)?
    a. God loves the whole world.
    b. God loved us before we loved Him.
    c. God's love is everlasting.
    d. God's love overlooks sin.

6. The wrath of God is as real as His love. What are the objects of God's wrath (select three)?
   a. all ungodliness and unrighteousness of men
   b. the hard, unrepenting heart
   c. the disobedient
   d. the forgiven sinner

7. Match the following characteristics of God with the definition on the left:

   ——Undeserved and freely-bestowed   a. Grace (Ephesians 2:8; Titus 2:11)
   favor toward others.

   ——Active pity or compassion toward   b. Holiness (Psalm 99:9; Revelation 15:4)
   offenders or the needy.

   ——Completely lacking in impurity or evil.   c. Mercy (Psalm 103:8; Ephesians 2:4)
   Set apart from all other beings.

   ——Impartiality or fairness in dealings   d. Righteousness/Justice (Nehemiah 9:33;
   with others.   Genesis 18:25)

8. When the Bible says God is holy, it means (select one)
   a. He is sinless.
   b. He hates sin and loves all that is good.
   c. He is separate from sinners.
   d. all of the above.

9. *What do you say?* Carefully think through the characteristics of God that you studied above. Which are particularly comforting to you?

   Are there any that disturb you? Why or why not?

   Often people say, "I think God would do this" or "I don't think He would do that." Why is it important to understand the character of God before speculating on what He might or might not do?

10. *What do others say?* Contact at least three people this week and ask them the following questions. You may wish to say something like the following:

    "I'm involved in a Bible Survey here in (name city). Could you help me by sharing your opinion on three important questions? (1) What are some characteristics of God that men do not share? (2) What does it mean that God is holy? (3) How do you account for the Biblical description of God as both a God of love and a God of wrath? Thank you so much for your help. Would you like for me to mail/e-mail you a copy of the survey results? Thank you."

    Record their names and addresses on the 3x5 cards provided by the class leader. Record the answers on the back, indicating if survey results are desired. Then return the cards next class meeting. Results of the survey will be tabulated by the class leader and mailed to each person indicating an interest.

"WHAT IS MAN, THAT THOU ART MINDFUL OF HIM?" asks the Psalmist (Psalm 8:4). Our bodies come from the dust and return to dust (Genesis 3:19). What are we? Why are we significant? What is our purpose in life? The answers to such questions will profoundly affect our outlook and the way we live.

Man's Origin

Many have suggested that man is simply one of many life forms that came into existence in the universe by accident. They say he is but a "higher animal," the "pinnacle of evolution;" he has a passing life that has no lasting significance. Men have responded to this theory by living as mere animals, by selfishly grasping for every pleasure at hand and by living in despair while awaiting entry into nothingness.

Others have a mystical view that life is a kind of cosmic wheel, endlessly revolving. They say that life always existed in some form. Man appears, dies, merges into a kind of "nothingness" and then is "reincarnated" in some other form. There is no explanation for origin, no directing intelligence, no personal God.

Contrast these two systems of belief. Which seems the more intelligent?

Belief in Origin by Chance

1. Originally there was nothing. Matter or energy came into existence uncaused, then formed entire planetary systems, all by chance.

2. Life began spontaneously in various planetary systems. It developed from simple to more complex forms by mindless direction. There was no designer or intelligence behind it.

Belief in Supreme Creator

1. God created the universe, including the earth, man, animals, sea life, birds and other creatures. (Genesis 1:1; 2:25; John 1:3; Colossians 1:16; Hebrews 11:3.)

2. God, the Supreme Intelligence, is the source of design, order and laws. He is the source of all life. Man is His special creation made in His spiritual image and likeness.

3. Man evolved from an ancient ancestor similar to the apes. He is an animal without any spiritual nature, a biological accident in space, with no purpose, no future.

3. All mankind has descended from the original human beings created by God, described in Genesis 1-2. Men differ from animals in their capacity to spiritually know and worship God, in having articulate speech and written communication, in having a soul and spirit that will never cease to exist.

The Bible says, "In the beginning God created the heaven and the earth . . . God created man" (Genesis 1:1, 27). "It is He that hath made us, and not we ourselves" (Psalm 100:3). We were known to God prior to our birth (Psalm 139:13-16). Why did He make us? It was for His own pleasure (Colossians 1:16; Revelation 4:11). He was the Potter and we were the clay (Romans 9:20-21). What is our purpose here? We are created to glorify God (Romans 1:21; Psalm 86:9, 12; Matthew 5:16). Yet man has refused to worship and serve his Creator (Romans 1:25). He has sought instead to live for self.

Man's Nature

Man is made in the image and likeness of God (Genesis 1:26; 5:1; 9:6). This means "shadow" or "resemblance." Since God is a Spirit, the resemblance is not physical but spiritual (Ephesians 4:24; Colossians 3:10). This is the chief aspect of the uniqueness of man. Man has a material aspect called the body, which in many respects is like the bodies of other creatures in its functions. Yet this is merely the "tent" or "earthly house" in which he lives (2 Corinthians 5:1-4; 2 Peter 1:13-14). More significantly, he has a soul and a spirit, together forming his triune being (1 Thessalonians 5:23). Distinguishing the soul from the spirit is difficult (Hebrews 4:12).

The body has to do with sensory contact with our surroundings. It is therefore called the seat of *world-consciousness*. The soul is the center of emotion, reason and decision (Psalm 13:2; 42:5). It is the seat of *self-consciousness*. The spirit has to do with our ability to know God and the things which pertain to the spiritual realm. It is the seat of *God-consciousness* (Romans 8:16). Even a person who does not know God has a spirit (James 2:26).

The inner being of man is sometimes called the "heart" (Deuteronomy 29:4; Psalm 40:8, 10, 12; Proverbs 14:10; Isaiah 44:18). Desires, perceptions and inner attitudes are seen as coming from this source. Conscience, as we know by common reference, is a sensitivity to what is right or wrong, good or evil (Romans 2:15; Hebrews 5:14). It speaks to our sense of duty or responsibility, as well as to our moral sense. We often say, "let your conscience be your guide." Certainly it is wise never to violate conscience even if it is weak or oversensitive (1 Corinthians 8:10). Yet a conscience may be good (Acts 23:1; 1 Timothy 1:5, 19; Hebrews 13:18) or it may be evil (1 Timothy 4:2; Hebrews 10:22). It may be pure (1 Timothy 3:9; 2 Timothy 1:3) or it may be defiled (Titus 1:15). It should be kept without offense (Acts 24:16).

Man's Choosing

The need to decide a matter, to cast one's lot, especially in the realm of the moral and the spiritual, is the most serious duty of man's conscience. It can and will affect our eternal destiny. God has clearly given man the right to choose and has made it the basis of righteous judgment (Deuteronomy 30:15, 19; Joshua 24:15; Revelation 20:12-13). Man enjoys choosing, but does not like to bear the consequences of bad choices. He blames God, parents, society, various institutions and the passing of events in order to shift responsibility from himself even while continuing to make evil choices.

Some religious systems teach that man is a moral robot designed by a God who determines everything and gives him no real chance to choose. But there is no ground for that teaching. God appeals to man to choose, and says that if he turns away from Him, he is without excuse (Romans 1:20).

Man's Fall

Thoughtful people have realized for thousands of years that something has gone wrong with man. Even certain types of animals show an ability to live in harmony and cooperation among their own kind. Why does man kill, hate, act brutally, let others starve and die? Why is selfishness and misconduct evident in the smallest children, without anyone teaching them these things? Why do children have to be taught to do good, while it is unnecessary to teach them to do evil? Theories about environment, parental habits, psychological forces, political and social systems have all been proposed. Yet no one has been able to prove their propositions or successfully change the nature of man by their theories.

The Scripture tells us what has gone wrong. The first human beings had an ideal environment and made the improper choice of disobeying God (Genesis 3). It was at this point that sin entered into the world (Romans 5:12-19), and with it a chain of dire consequences. Judgment was swift because man was plainly guilty (Genesis 3:16-24). It resulted in the loss of that perfect environment, and the certainty of physical death, pain and difficulty for man and his descendants down to the present day. It has been called the Fall of Man. The consequences of this fall are detailed for us in Genesis 6:5; 8:21; Psalm 12:1-3; Romans 3:10-23 and other passages.

The continuing effects are seen in man's nature even today. Sin has clouded his spiritual understanding (Ephesians 4:18; 1 Corinthians 2:14), given him a deceitful heart (Jeremiah 17:9) and defiled his flesh and spirit alike (Ephesians 2:3). The Bible attributes all human conflicts, sorrows and evil to one source—sin—and says that it permeates the very nature of man. It also states that it has affected the entire creation in a physical sense, from thorns in the botanical creation to violence in the animal kingdom.

Man's Responsibility

Man is responsible to a loving and caring God. God greatly values man (Matthew 10:31) and counts him worthy of the greatest sacrifice (John 3:16). This loving concern is seen in the attitude of Jesus as He wept over a city which had rejected Him (Luke 19:41). He was willing to save them, but the inhabitants refused (Luke 13:34).

Man is not independent and self-governing (autonomous), although he sometimes thinks and acts this way. He came from the hand of a Creator and Sustainer on Whom he is dependent for even a breath (Isaiah 42:5). Man must some day face his Creator and give account (Romans 14:12; Hebrews 9:27). Two alternatives are stated in John 3:36 and 1 John 5:12. Man must choose.

UNDERSTANDING MAN   LESSON 4

It is important to know the nature of our humanity: where we came from, why we exist and what is the cause of our problems.

1. Man's origin is (select one)
    a. through evolution from lower forms of life.
    b. a mystery which we cannot understand.
    c. from the creating hand of God.
    d. part of a cycle of existence, without beginning.

2. We exist (select one)
    a. to fulfill our personal destiny.
    b. to develop our own potential.
    c. to enjoy life the best we can.
    d. solely to glorify God.

3. What is the function or activity in man of the following:

    a. the body:

    b. the soul:

    c. the spirit:

4. What is the meaning to you of the likeness mentioned in Genesis 1:26 and 5:1? In what way are we like Him?

5. What evidence do you see in the world to support the teaching of the Bible that man is a sinner by nature and choice?

6. The free will of man or his ability to choose:
   a. is an illusion because God's purposes overrule.
   b. is so limited that he is not really responsible.
   c. gives man the right to choose to love and obey God.
   d. is made impossible because of difficult circumstances.

7. Paraphrase (rewrite in your own words) Psalm 139:14-16.

8. How do the following verses indicate that God has given man a right to choose and has made it the basis of righteous judgment (Deuteronomy 30:15, 19; Joshua 24:15; Revelation 20:12-13)?

9. *What do you say?* Summarize in your own words what you feel your own personal responsibility to God is. How can God get pleasure and glory out of your life?

10. *What do others say?* Contact at least three people this week and ask them the following questions. You may wish to say something like the following:

    "I'm involved in a Bible Survey here in (name city). Could you help me by sharing your opinion on three important questions? (1) Where did man come from? (2) For what purpose does man exist? (3) What do you feel is your number one purpose in life? Thank you so much for your help. Would you like for me to mail/e-mail you a copy of the survey results? Thank you."

    Record their names and addresses on the 3x5 cards provided by the class leader. Record the answers on the back, indicating if survey results are desired. Then return the three cards next class meeting. Results of the survey will be tabulated by the class leader and mailed to each person indicating an interest.

Why is there wickedness, sorrow, suffering, war, hatred in the world? Why is there greed, envy, pride and cruelty? Why do even children act selfishly, lie, disobey and bring grief to those closest to them without having anyone directly teaching them to do so? Is this only due to a bad environment? The Bible tells us that the root of man's condition begins from birth and is present before there are any outside influences on him (Psalm 51:5; 58:3). The problems of man cannot be properly understood without facing the problem of sin.

Common View of Sin

What is sin? A common dictionary will tell us that it is an offense against moral law or against the law of God. This is clear enough. Yet men have departed from this simple definition to introduce various strange ideas. Examples are:

1. There is No Sin.

Right or wrong is only a matter of changing social practice.

2. What Harms Someone Else is Sin,

but whatever you do personally is your own business.

3. Sin Has to Do With Various Bad Habits.

These are viewed by different groups in different ways.

4. Sin is Wrong Thinking or Bad Judgment.

5. Sin Displeases God But is Not Serious.

Everyone does it and we are only human.

Biblical View of Sin

These ideas may be contrasted with what the Bible teaches sin is:

1. Turning to our own way (Isaiah 53:6).

2. Breaking the law of God (1 John 3:4).

3. Rebellion against God or lawlessness (1 John 3:4 NASB).

4. Knowing to do good and failing to do it (James 4:17).

5. Acting other than according to faith (Romans 14:23).

6. Not believing in Jesus (John 16:9).

7. All unrighteousness or wrongdoing (1 John 5:17).

8. Anything contrary to God's character (Romans 3:23).

Various evil things which come from within the heart of man are listed in Mark 7:21-23 (NASB) such as evil thoughts, fornication, adultery, coveting, envy, slander, pride and foolishness. No sins are hidden from God (Psalm 90:8). They spring from a sinful nature (Romans 7:18). Our sins are an offense against God because He is absolutely holy (Psalm 145:17; Isaiah 6:3-5; Habakkuk 1:13). If there were no God, then there would be no sin, for there would be no perfect Being to be the standard for what is right.

The Origin and Results of Sin

The first recorded instance of sin took place in heaven. The angel Lucifer desired to be equal with God (Isaiah 14:12-14). His sin was pride (Ezekiel 28:15-17). For this sin he was cast out of heaven and became the devil. Through his temptation of the first human family, he introduced sin into the world. That sin was disobedience to God (Genesis 2:16-17; 3:1-6). Man was held responsible for sin and judged accordingly (Genesis 3:16-24).

It will be seen in Genesis 3 that the first human beings lost their fellowship with God. Their judgment was separation from His presence. They became liable for the first time to physical death, which is separation of the soul from the body. They immediately experienced spiritual death, which is separation of the soul from fellowship with God. They discovered the truth of the classic Bible statement, "The wages of sin is death" (Romans 6:23). Wages are what we earn and deserve.

"The soul that sinneth, it shall die" (Ezekiel 18:4). Death alone is the payment for sin. This death includes the second death (Revelation 20:14), which means eternal separation from God. The sins of men are recorded in heaven and will be used as a basis of judgment (Revelation 20:12). Money, prayer, church attendance and good deeds will not pay the debt of sin.

God Loves and Receives Sinners

It is amazingly true that a holy God, with all His hatred for sin, still loves the sinner. "God commendeth His love toward us, in that while we were yet sinners, Christ died for us" (Romans 5:8). It is "not that we loved God, but that He loved us" (1 John 4:10). He demonstrated this love by sending His only-begotten Son to save us (John 3:16). Through the death of His Son for us God is able to offer forgiveness (Acts 13:38; Ephesians 1:7).

The acknowledgment of sin must precede any true desire for forgiveness. The Psalmist cried, "I acknowledge my transgressions: and my sin is ever before me" (Psalm 51:3). He cried out for cleansing and denied nothing of his offense toward God. The lost son said, "I will arise and go to my father, and will say unto him, Father, I have sinned against heaven and before thee" (Luke 15:18).

Our Savior told a story of two men who prayed. One man would not so much as lift up his eyes to heaven, but rather he smote his breast and cried, "God, be merciful to me, a sinner." Jesus pronounced this man justified (Luke 18:13-14). God's Holy Spirit works to bring the inner conviction of sin (John 16:8-11).

God Calls Sinners to Repentance

"I came not to call the righteous, but sinners to repentance," said Jesus (Luke 5:32). The convicting work of the Spirit brings men to repentance (John 16:8). The simple meaning of this word is "change of mind." In Scripture, its usage involves a change of mind with the intent to turn from sin, in order to turn to God. The Old Testament call was "Turn ye" (Zechariah 1:3). It is only God's goodness that leads us to repentance (Romans 2:4). There is no lightness about sin, but rather sorrow (2 Corinthians 7:9-10). Repentance works to bring about genuine change, rather than empty words (Matthew 3:8; Luke 13:3, 5; Acts 26:20).

Early Christian preaching commanded men to repent (Acts 2:38; 3:19; 17:30). Such an act is not one that earns our way to God, but one that acknowledges our wretched condition. Repentance towards God and faith towards our Lord Jesus Christ are companion acts of a right response to God (Acts 20:21). Repentance is not a work which earns salvation. It is a response towards God which acknowledges the seriousness of the offense and desires to change (Isaiah 55:7).

Need for Self-Examination

It is important to know that we are lost if we are ever to meet our Savior (Luke 19:10). That lostness is due to sin—of which we must repent in turning to God.

Check List:
1. Have you always been unselfish?
2. Have you always been free of envy and covetousness?
3. Have you unfailingly done every good you could do?
4. Have you always been kind and thoughtful to everyone?
5. Have you always loved God with all your heart, soul, mind and strength?
6. Have you always loved others just as yourself?
7. Have you always been as perfect as the Lord Jesus Christ?

If the answer to any of these is "NO," the Bible says you are a sinner. To have kept the whole law and be guilty of one violation is to be guilty of all (James 2:10). One violation of the perfect holiness of God makes a person a sinner.

The Lord Jesus came to "save His people from their sins" (Matthew 1:21). The penalty and power of sin is dreadful. The possibility of the second death is awesome. The Psalmist writes, "Blessed is he whose transgression is forgiven, whose sin is covered. Blessed is the man unto whom the Lord imputeth not iniquity" (Psalm 32:1-2).

It is well for a person who professes to be a Christian, but who practices sin as a way of life, to ponder this question: "If a man is not saved from his sins, from what is he saved?"

THE PROBLEM OF SIN

The following questions may help clarify man's greatest problem.

1. Write a definition of sin in your own words after considering Matthew 5:28; Romans 3:23; James 4:17 and 1 John 3:4.

    Paraphrase (rewrite in your own words) Isaiah 53:6.

2. According to Isaiah 14:12-14 and Ezekiel 28:15-17, sin originated in the heavens and had its roots in (select one)
    a. pride.
    b. lack of good judgment.
    c. a misunderstanding.

3. According to Genesis 2:17; 3:1-6, the first recorded sin on earth had its roots in (select one)
    a. unbelief and disobedience.
    b. lust and immorality.
    c. anger and frustration.
    d. a misunderstanding.

4. What is God's attitude toward sin (Habakkuk 1:13)?

    What payment did God require for sin in Old Testament times (Ezekiel 18:20)? In New Testament times (Romans 6:23)?

5. There are three types of death mentioned in Scripture: (a) physical death (separation of the soul from the body); (b) spiritual death (separation of man's spirit from God's spirit); (c) the "second death" (eternal separation of man's spirit from God's spirit, occurring when a man dies physically while still in a state of spiritual death).

    Match the verses on the right with the three types of death on the left:

    _____ physical death   a. Ephesians 2:1-3

    _____ spiritual death   b. Hebrews 9:27

    _____ "second death"   c. Revelation 20:11-15

6. According to Romans 5:8, whom did Christ die for? There are two types of sinners as illustrated by Luke 18:10-14: those who admit that they are sinners and those who do not. Why is it important to realize you are a sinner?

7. Repentance means (select one)
   a. a religious rite to be observed on certain days.
   b. a change of mind which results in a change of action.
   c. telling God you are sorry.
   d. we are unhappy with the way things turned out.

8. To receive God's forgiveness, we must (select one)
   a. acknowledge our sin.
   b. admit our responsibility for sin.
   c. cry to God for cleansing.
   d. be willing to forsake our sin.
   e. all of the above.

9. *What do you say?* How and when were you first convicted of sin and your need of a Savior?

10. *What do others say?* Contact at least three people this week and ask them the following questions. You may wish to say something like the following:

    "I'm involved in a Bible Survey here in (name city). Could you help me by sharing your opinion on three important questions? (1) In your opinion, what is sin? (2) Do you see anything in the newspapers or on television that indicates that man is a sinner? (3) What do you think a righteous God would do about sin? Thank you so much for your help. Would you like for me to mail/e-mail you a copy of the survey results? Thank you."

    Record their names and addresses on the 3x5 cards provided by the class leader. Record the answers on the back, indicating if survey results are desired. Then return the cards next class meeting. Results of the survey will be tabulated by the class leader and mailed to each person indicating an interest.

CONSIDERING ETERNITY

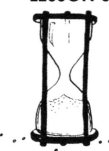

"BUT MAN DIETH, AND WASTETH AWAY: yea, man giveth up the ghost, and where is he?" (Job 14:10). Thoughtful people who are aware of the constant stream of funerals and obituaries realize that their time on earth is limited. They also pause to consider whether they have any hope of living beyond the short time span of this life. Others may try to ignore death and live as if it will never come. Of course, ignoring something will never change reality, but will merely avoid the pain of thinking about it. At one time or another the majority of the living ponder the question, "What happens after death?" Their theories fall under several headings:

1. Non-Existence.

We cease to exist. This is sometimes called "annihilation." "When you are dead, you are dead."

2. Reincarnation.

One comes back to earth as a different form of life or in the body of another person. Presumably this would require supernatural power of some kind.

3. Spirit Communication.

The dead live in a mysterious spirit world and may seek to maintain contact with those still living on earth.

4. Impossible to Know.

Our state after death is beyond human knowledge. It is questionable whether there is life after death or not. We must wait and see, trusting in either fate or our good life if there is an afterlife.

None of these theories properly can be made to fit the teachings of the Bible. The Bible presents those who have died as being conscious and aware, in one of two places: in the presence of God (2 Corinthians 5:8) in a state of blessedness (Revelation 14:13), or separated from God in a place of great torment (Revelation 20:10, 15).

Resurrection from the Dead

The very word "resurrection" means a "standing" or "rising up." The Lord Jesus answered those in His day who denied the resurrection by pointing out that God's name was attached to great men who had long been deceased. "He is not a God of the dead, but of the living" (Luke 20:37-38). Proclaiming the resurrection was foundational to apostolic preaching (Acts 1:22; 4:2; 17:18; 23:6). The Apostle Paul said there were more than 500 witnesses to the resurrection of Christ (1 Corinthians 15:4-8) and that if it were not true their faith was a vain thing (15:12-17). The striking truth of Scripture, however, is that there are two classes in the resurrection, carefully divided from one another.

"And many of them that sleep in the dust of the earth shall awake, some to *everlasting life*, and some to shame and *everlasting contempt*" (Daniel 12:2).

"All . . . shall come forth; they that have done good, unto the *resurrection of life*, and they that have done evil, unto the *resurrection of damnation*" (John 5:28-29).

"There shall be a resurrection of the dead, both of the just and unjust" (Acts 24:15b).

Two eventualities face men when the judgment by God is considered. *Eternal judgment* is one dread possibility (Hebrews 6:2; 9:27). The other is *eternal life* (John 3:16) and thereby freedom from that judgment of condemnation (John 5:24; Romans 8:1).

The Length of Eternity

It is strange that words in the Bible like "eternity," "everlasting," "forever and ever" should be taught to have a limitation. Yet some have gone back to the original languages of Scripture and sought to prove these expressions mean merely an extended or indefinite period. The uses of these words in Scripture make clear that there is no limit on the duration of eternity, even if translated "unto the ages of the ages."

The following verses make clear that the meanings of "eternal" or "everlasting" are the same in their various usages.

1. As Applied to God.
"The everlasting God" (Romans 16:26), "the eternal Spirit" (Hebrews 9:14), "His eternal glory" (1 Peter 5:10), "power everlasting" (1 Timothy 6:16), "everlasting kingdom" (2 Peter 1:11).

2. As Applied to the Believer's Future.
"Eternal redemption" (Hebrews 9:12), "eternal salvation" (Hebrews 5:9), "everlasting life" (John 3:16, 36), "life everlasting" (Luke 18:30), "eternal life" (John 3:15).

3. As Applied to the Unbeliever's Future.
"Everlasting fire" (Matthew 18:8), "everlasting punishment" (Matthew 25:46), "everlasting destruction" (2 Thessalonians 1:9), "eternal fire" (Jude 7).

The same comparisons exist when the phrase "forever and ever" is used. It is used of God and His throne (Revelation 4:9-10; 10:6; 15:7), of the believer's future reign with the Lord (Revelation 22:5), of endless torment (Revelation 14:11; 20:10).

Certain words have been presumed to mean annihilation, such as "destruction," "perish" and "consume." Yet it is plain the devil was destroyed (Hebrews 2:14) but not annihilated (Revelation 20:10). Believers may be consumed by the talk of others but not annihilated thereby (Galatians 5:15). The wastrel son felt he was perishing, yet he did not cease to exist as a person (Luke 15:17). The lot of the unsaved is everlasting destruction (2 Thessalonians 1:9). That the destruction is everlasting indicates that it does not involve a cessation of existence. There is loss of well-being (feeling well) but not loss of being (existence).

The Condition of the Lost

1. As Described by Jesus
The Lord Jesus told a story called The Rich Man in Hell, which some describe as a parable (Luke 16:19-31). Yet it is not called a parable in the Bible. However, even if it were a parable, the use of figurative language would not nullify the truth that is taught in this passage. The Savior sought to teach something in this story and we would do well to ponder the lessons:
    a. There was no cessation of existence after death.
    b. There was no unconsciousness or sleep of their souls.
    c. There was no salvation of all men.
    d. There was no second chance offered.
    e. There was no reincarnation or coming back to earth.
    f. There was no end of torment or hope of change for the unsaved man.
    g. There was no purpose of purification, only of eternal punishment.

2. As Further Taught by Jesus
The terrifying descriptions listed below were all given by the One who loved with the greatest of all loves and gave Himself to save men. He simply described the truth about those who leave this world neglecting or refusing Him.
    a. Fire that is unquenchable (Matthew 3:12; 18:8; Mark 9:44, 48)
    b. Torment forever (Revelation 14:11)
    c. Outer darkness (Matthew 22:13; 25:30)
    d. Wailing and gnashing of teeth (Matthew 13:42, 50; 24:51; Luke 13:28)
    e. Lake of fire (Revelation 20:15)

Objections to Teaching of Eternal Punishment
There are several objections to this unpopular doctrine.

1. It is Incompatible With the Love of God.
"As I live, saith the Lord God, I have no pleasure in the death of the wicked; but that the wicked turn from his way and live: turn ye . . . from your evil ways; for why will ye die?" (Ezekiel 33:11). The Lord Jesus beheld a city which had rejected Him and wept over it (Luke 19:41). He is indeed a loving God, but He cannot righteously clear the guilty who reject His salvation (Numbers 14:18).

2. Appealing to Fear is Not a Good Motive.
It may be true that love of God or desire for the best are better motives, yet fear of serious consequences is a common preventative for misconduct or

injury even in everyday living. The Lord Jesus plainly appealed to the fear of God and His coming judgment (Matthew 10:28). Fearing God is said to be the beginning of wisdom (Proverbs 9:10). Throughout the Scriptures men are exhorted, in the proper sense, to fear God (1 Peter 2:17; Revelation 14:7; 15:4).

3. It is Unfair of God to Be So Severe.

Men who have been offered a way of escape by a God who loves them and who have responded by refusal, evasion and procrastination, need not be surprised when they receive certain justice from an outraged holiness. "Be not deceived; God is not mocked: for whatsoever a man soweth, that shall he also reap" (Galatians 6:7). Insulting the infinite love and patience of an infinite God demands an infinite retribution.

The Condition of the Redeemed

The final state of the righteous is in vivid contrast to the above. "In thy presence is fullness of joy; at thy right hand there are pleasures for evermore" (Psalm 16:11). "Blessed are the dead which die in the Lord" (Revelation 14:13). The believer looks "for a city which hath foundations, whose builder and maker is God" (Hebrews 11:10). This place is better than anything of which the world has any knowledge. The eternal state and abode of the believer is further described below:

1. It is With Christ.

"I go and prepare a place for you . . . that where I am, there ye may be also" (John 14:3; cf. 17:24). To be absent from the body is to "be present with the Lord" (2 Corinthians 5:8).

2. It is in a Changed Body.

It will be like His body (Philippians 3:21) and therefore incorruptible (1 Corinthians 15:35-44). We will be recognizable as was the Lord (Matthew 28:9, 17; Luke 24:31, 39-40). The resurrection of the body for those in Christ will take place at the Second Coming of Christ (1 Thessalonians 4:15-17).

3. It is in a Place of "No Mores."

There is no more death, sorrow, crying, pain and all that makes life difficult and unhappy (Revelation 21:4).

4. It is in a Place of Infinite Beauty.

"The city was pure gold, like unto clear glass" (Revelation 21:18-21). It is adorned with all manner of precious stones.

5. It is in a Place Where Nothing Unholy or Defiling Enters
(Revelation 21:27).

The place of the redeemed is sometimes termed the "New Jerusalem." We call it Heaven. The Jewish believer called it "Paradise" or "Abraham's Bosom" before Jesus came and died. By whatever term, it should be the subject of yearning for every believer. As Paul said, "to die is gain" (Philippians 1:21). How wonderful it was when the Lord Jesus said to the thief on the cross who repented of his sins and believed on Him, "Today shalt thou be with me in paradise" (Luke 23:43). Will you be there with Him?

CONSIDERING ETERNITY   LESSON 6

"If a man die, shall he live again?" This question, posed by one of the ancients, is still of great importance today. What happens after death?

1. The Bible presents those who have died as being conscious and aware in one of two places. What are they (2 Corinthians 5:8; Revelation 20:10, 15)?

2. The Bible further indicates that all who die will be resurrected (raised up) from the dead. Describe the two different destinies of mankind (Daniel 12:2; John 5:28-29; Acts 24:15b).

3. Paraphrase (rewrite in your own words) the following verses: John 3:16; 2 Thessalonians 1:8-9.

4. How long is eternity? Can you think of an illustration to describe it?

5. Jesus told about a man who went to hell (Luke 16:19-31). According to this passage, which of the following is true (select one)?
    a. A person simply ceases to be when he dies.
    b. A dead person experiences a state of unconsciousness or "soul sleep."
    c. Hell is a place of conscious, never-ending torment.
    d. All men will be saved.
    e. If a person goes to hell, he will get a second chance.

6. Which of the following did Jesus not use to describe hell (select one)?
    a. Fire that is unquenchable
    b. Torment forever
    c. Outer darkness
    d. Wailing and gnashing of teeth
    e. A place of temporary purification
    f. Lake of fire

7. How would you answer the following objections?
   a. The doctrine of hell is incompatible with the love of God.

   b. This teaching appeals to fear.

   c. It is unfair of God to be so severe.

8. The Bible describes the future of the believer in heaven as (select one):
   a. Being with Christ forever.
   b. Existence in a changed body.
   c. Being free from sorrow and pain.
   d. Being in a place where nothing unholy enters.
   e. All of the above.
   f. A and C above.

9. *What do you say?* Have you ever come to the place in your own spiritual experience where you knew for certain that if you were to die tonight, you would go to heaven? Explain.

10. *What do others say?* Contact at least three people this week and ask them the following questions. You may wish to say something like the following:

    "I'm involved in a Bible Survey here in (name city). Could you help me by sharing your opinion on three important questions? (1) In your opinion, what happens to a person when he dies? (2) What do the expressions "heaven" and "hell" mean to you? (3) If you could ask any question about the afterlife and get an absolutely reliable answer, what would you ask? Thank you so much for your help. Would you like for me to mail/e-mail a copy of the survey results? Thank you."

    Record their names and addresses on the 3x5 cards provided by the class leader. Record the answers on the back, indicating if the survey results are desired. Then return the cards next class meeting. Results of the survey will be tabulated by the class leader and mailed to each person indicating an interest.

"I KNOW THAT MESSIAH IS COMING . . . who is called Christ," said the woman of Samaria. "Jesus said to her, 'I who speak to you am He'" (John 4:25-26 RSV). A short time earlier a Galilean fisherman said to his brother, "We have found the Messiah, which means Christ" (John 1:41 RSV). He was the One who would "bring in everlasting righteousness" by establishing His everlasting kingdom. Jesus of Nazareth was born almost 2,000 years ago and His birth is now the dividing point of all history. He was recognized as the Anointed One prophesied by the Holy Scriptures of Old. He came as:

1. The promised King and Deliverer of the Jewish people (2 Samuel 7:11-13).
2. The One sent by God to be the Savior of the world (Luke 2:11; John 4:42).
3. "God with us" (Imanuel, Emmanuel), a Divine Deliverer (Matthew 1:23; Isaiah 7:14).

Prophecies Concerning Jesus Christ

The significance of Jesus Christ (Jesus the Messiah) cannot be denied in terms of His life and impact on world history. It is without equal. It is supported by a mass of evidence from Old Testament Scripture, written long before His birth. Identification is completed by matching each and every prophecy with the details of His life. There are over 200 of them, of which the following are examples:

1. Seed of the Woman (Genesis 3:15; Galatians 4:4).
2. Birth at Bethlehem (Micah 5:2; Matthew 2:1, 4-6).
3. His virgin birth (Isaiah 7:14; Matthew 1:18, 23-25).
4. His forerunner (Isaiah 40:3; Matthew 3:1-3).
5. His entry into Jerusalem (Zechariah 9:9; Luke 19:35-38).
6. His rejection (Isaiah 53:3; Psalm 69:8; John 7:5; 19:15).
7. His betrayal (Zechariah 11:12; Matthew 10:4; 26:14-15).
8. Struck, spat upon (Isaiah 50:6; Matthew 26:67).
9. Suffering for the sins of others (Isaiah 53:5; 1 Peter 2:24; 3:18).
10. Pierced on the cross (Psalm 22:16; Zechariah 12:10; John 19:34, 37).
11. Praying for His enemies (Isaiah 53:12; Luke 23:34).
12. Crucified with criminals (Isaiah 53:9, 12; Matthew 27:38).
13. Buried in tomb of rich (Isaiah 53:9; Matthew 27:57-60).
14. Rising from the dead (Psalm 16:8-10; Luke 24:46; Acts 13:33-35).

The same Scriptures prophesy His coming again (Psalm 50:3-6; Daniel 7:13; Zechariah 12:10; 14:4, plus many New Testament references). They predict His universal rule (1 Chronicles 17:11-14; Isaiah 9:7; Daniel 7:14; Psalm 2:6-8; 45:6-7; 72:8; 110:1-3).

The Offices of Jesus Christ

The Lord Jesus uniquely combined in Himself the three great offices that come from God.

1. He is a Prophet.

He is the greatest of them all (Mark 6:4; Acts 3:22). He was the very One of whom Moses spoke (Deuteronomy 18:15-19).

2. He is a Great High Priest.

He represents His people before the Father and prays for them (Hebrews 4:14-16; 7:25). He was spoken of in 1 Samuel 2:35.

3. He is a King, the King of Kings

(Revelation 19:16). He came at first as King of the Jews (John 19:19). He is King today in the hearts of His people. He will be acknowledged by all in a coming day (Philippians 2:9-10).

The Deity of Jesus Christ

The Bible declares that Jesus Christ was God revealed in flesh (1 Timothy 3:16). He was the exact likeness of the unseen God (Colossians 1:15). How amazing that the living God came in the flesh (John 1:1, 14). How sad it was that "He was in the world, and the world was made by Him, and the world knew Him not!" (John 1:10).

It was necessary that God save us. Only He had the power. "I, even I, am the Lord; and beside Me there is no Savior" (Isaiah 43:11). He came as Jesus of Nazareth to be our "great God and our Savior" (Titus 2:13). Mary said, "My spirit hath rejoiced in God my Savior" (Luke 1:47). The man-child to be born from her womb was her Savior and God. The Biblical references that point to Jesus as God are many.

1. He is Directly Called God

(John 1:1, 14; 20:28; Romans 9:5; 2 Peter 1:1; 1 John 5:20). The Father addresses the Son as God (Hebrews 1:8).

2. He is Called the Son of God.

His hearers clearly understood this claim to mean that He was God (John 10:33-36). There is a lesser use of the term "son of God," but He is the unique (only-begotten) Son of God (John 1:14, 18).

3. All the Fullness of God Dwells in Him

(Colossians 1:19; 2:9). He is not a lesser form of God.

4. He Bears the Divine Names of God.

He is called the Alpha and Omega, the First and Last, the Beginning and End (Revelation 22:13; 1:8, 17; Isaiah 44:6). He is also the I AM (John 8:24, 58; Exodus 3:14). To say of himself "I AM" is a self-declaration of His Deity.

5. He is Worshipped As God

(Matthew 14:33; John 20:28; Philippians 2:10; Hebrews 1:6; Isaiah 45:23). This is exclusively for God (Matthew 4:10; Revelation 22:8-9).

6. He is to be Equally Honored

(John 5:23). God does not give His glory to another (Isaiah 42:8).

7. He Has the Divine Offices.

He is Creator (Colossians 1:16-17; Hebrews 1:2, 10). He is the Judge of all (John 5:22). He is the forgiver of sins (Matthew 9:2-6), yet only God does this (Isaiah 43:25).

8. He Has Life Within Himself

(John 5:26). He gives life to others but He is self-existent.

9. He Has All Divine Attributes.

He is unchangeable (Hebrews 13:8). He has all-power (Revelation 1:8), all-presence (Matthew 28:20), all-knowledge (John 21:17), eternity (Micah 5:2; 1 Timothy 1:16-17), and all other divine qualities.

10. He Did the Works of God.

He commanded the elements (Matthew 8:26-27; Mark 4:39-41). He created food for the multitude (Matthew 14:19-21; 15:36-38). He raised the dead (John 11:32-44; Luke 7:12-16).

The Humanity of Jesus Christ

Though He was fully and eternally God, He was also "the *man* Christ Jesus" (1 Timothy 2:5). Jesus often referred to Himself as the Son of Man. He took on humanity to become like us in all things except sin. He experienced our emotions. He hungered, thirsted, suffered, wept and was weary. He experienced temptation by the devil (Matthew 4:1-11). He suffered, bled, died, was buried and rose again from the dead. He was different from ordinary men, yet fully human.

1. He Had Human Parents,

tracing back through David to Adam (Luke 3:23-38), *but* He was born of a virgin through a conception by the Holy Spirit (Matthew 1:18-23).

2. He Had a Normal Body,

in appearance like others (Romans 8:3; John 4:9). He grew to manhood in normal fashion (Luke 2:40, 52), *but* His life was untainted by sin (Hebrews 4:15).

3. He Was a Triune Being,

as others. He had a body (Hebrews 10:5), a soul (Matthew 26:38) and a spirit (Luke 23:46); *but* He exhibited a unique God-consciousness, communing intimately with the Father as no other man.

Many of His utterances can only be understood from the standpoint of His humanity—His cry on the cross (Matthew 27:46), and His very death. The most important question that Jesus asked of men was "Whom say ye that I am?" (Matthew 16:15). He said that if they did not believe rightly about Him, they would die in their sins (John 8:24). Who do you say Jesus is?

JESUS THE MESSIAH: GOD'S PROVISION   LESSON 7

Jesus asked, "Whom do you say that I am?" It was of the utmost importance that people recognize Him fully and acknowledge His identity. Test yourself.

1. Whom was the Samaritan woman looking for to reveal to her the truth of God (John 4:25)? How did Jesus respond to her statement (John 4:26)?

2. The coming of Messiah (translated "Christ" in Greek) was foretold hundreds of years before the Old Testament writings. Match the following verses on the right with the prophecy on the left.

   _____ Birth at Bethlehem   a. Isaiah 7:14; Matthew 1:18,23-25
   _____ His virgin birth   b. Isaiah 40:3; Matthew 3:1-3
   _____ His forerunner   c. Isaiah 53:5; 1 Peter 2:24; 3:18
   _____ His entry into Jerusalem   d. Isaiah 53:9, 12; Matthew 27:38
   _____ His betrayal   e. Isaiah 53:9; Matthew 27:57-60
   _____ Suffering for the sins of others   f. Micah 5:2; Matthew 2:1, 4-6
   _____ Pierced on the cross   g. Psalm 16:8-10; Luke 24:46; Acts 13:33-35
   _____ Crucified with criminals   h. Psalm 22:16; Zechariah 12:10; John 19:34,37
   _____ Buried in tomb of rich   i. Zechariah 9:9; Luke 19:35-38
   _____ Rising from the dead   j. Zechariah 11:12; Matthew 10:4; 26:14-15

3. Identify the three great offices of Messiah (Christ):

   a. Deuteronomy 18:15-19, Mark 6:4

   b. 1 Samuel 2:35; Hebrews 4:14-16; 7:25

   c. Revelation 19:16; John 19:19; Philippians 2:9-10

4. In what ways was Jesus like other men while on earth?

   How does it help you to understand that Jesus experienced common human emotions?

   How was Jesus different from other men while on earth (as described in the following verses)?

   Matthew 1:23

   John 8:46

   John 7:46

   Mark 4:37-41

   Luke 7:22

5. What attributes (qualities) of deity (God) are ascribed to Jesus Christ in the following verses?

Matthew 28:20

Mark 2:5-7

1 Timothy 1:17

Hebrews 13:8

Revelation 1:8

6. Answer by circling True or False.
   a. God the Father addressed Jesus as God. (Hebrews 1:8) (True or False)
   b. Jesus refused to allow men to worship Him. (Matthew 14:33; John 20:28-29) (True or False)
   c. The Lord Jesus never claimed to be God. (John 8:58; 10:30) (True or False)

7. When Jesus was born on earth (select one)
   a. He ceased to be God when He became man.
   b. He united in His own Person both deity and humanity.
   c. He was not truly human because He was God.
   d. His true father was Joseph just as His true mother was Mary.

8. Paraphrase (rewrite in your own words) John 1:1-3, 14.

9. *What do you say?* Philippians 2:9-11 indicates that every creature will "bow the knee" to Christ at a future time. How and when will you do this in your life?

10. *What do others say?* Contact at least three people this week and ask them the following questions. You may wish to say something like the following:

    "I'm involved in a Bible Survey here in (name city). Could you help me by sharing your opinion on three important questions? (1) Who is Jesus Christ? (2) The Bible teaches that God became a man. If you were given an opportunity to be with Him, what would you expect Him to be like? (3) Do the expressions "Son of God" and "God the Son" mean the same thing to you? Please explain this. Thank you so much for your help. Would you like for me to mail/e-mail you a copy of the survey results? Thank you."

    Record their names and addresses on the 3x5 cards provided by the class leader. Record the answers on the back, indicating if survey results are desired. Then return the cards next class meeting. Results of the survey will be tabulated by the class leader and mailed to each person indicating an interest.

The cross is the great symbol of the Christian faith. It was upon a cross that our Savior died. God has ordained the "preaching of the cross" (1 Corinthians 1:17-18). Millions have been taught that Christ died on the cross for our sins. But what does this mean? Why was it necessary? What did it accomplish? These questions often leave those who profess to be Christians in a state of confusion.

The Necessity of the Cross

Why was Christ's death upon the cross necessary? Consider this:

1. God is Righteous and Holy (1 Peter 1:16; Isaiah 6:2-3).

Nothing that defiles can enter His presence (Revelation 21:27).

2. Sin Must Be Judged (Romans 2:3, 12).

He can by no means clear the guilty (Exodus 34:7; Job 10:14). All the world is guilty before God (Romans 3:19). Sin demands capital punishment, which is death (Romans 6:23).

The penalty must be paid. The problem for God was how to be entirely just and yet be able to justify the sinner (Romans 3:26). How could the righteousness and truth of God be reconciled with His mercy?

The Principle of Substitution

When one person or thing takes the place of another it is called substitution. The substitution of animals in place of the sinner was a feature of approach to God in the Old Testament. The Passover lamb was sacrificed in death as a protection against the judgment of God (Exodus 12:3-17). Millions of such sacrifices were offered to God, according to His commandment. Such offerings made what was called "atonement" (Leviticus 5:10). This meant that sin was "covered" by the death of the innocent victim.

It is important to note that John the Baptist publicly hailed Jesus as the "Lamb of God which taketh away the sin of the world" (John 1:29). He saw in Jesus the One who would be the true sacrificial victim and toward whom all previous sacrifices had been pointing. He was to be the one true and final Substitute. The prophets clearly predicted that the coming Messiah would be stricken by God for the sins of others and thus bear all their judgment (Isaiah 53:4-6). It is the heart of the Christian proclamation that "Christ died for our sins according to the Scriptures" (1 Corinthians 15:3).

The Scriptures which teach this substitutionary death should be carefully studied (Romans 5:6-8; 1 Peter 2:24; 3:18). The Savior took the place of the sinner. The just took the place of the unjust. The innocent took the place of the guilty. The death of Jesus was not just a moral example. Our offenses demanded it (Romans 4:25). It was according to the counsel of God (Acts 2:23). He was the willing victim and no man took His life from Him (John 10:17-18). He gave Himself for us (Galatians 1:4), was made sin for us (2 Corinthians 5:21). He was made a curse for us (Galatians 3:13).

Thus Jesus bought, or redeemed, us (1 Peter 1:18-19; Matthew 20:28). He made peace through the blood of His cross (Colossians 1:20). The sinner has been justified, or declared righteous, and has been reconciled to God by the death of Jesus (Romans 5:9-10).

The Perfection of the Sacrifice

Sacrifice is a word repeatedly used in the Bible and is at the heart of the Christian message. The sacrificial death of the Lord Jesus may be considered in various ways.

1. Blood Sacrifice (Hebrews 9:22).
Without the shedding of blood, there is no remission, or forgiveness, of sins.

2. Human Sacrifice (Hebrews 9:12-14; 10:4).
Only a man can die in place of another man in satisfying God's justice.

3. Sinless Sacrifice (Hebrews 4:15; 1 Peter 1:19; John 8:29, 46).
Only the One without sin can die for the sins of another.

4. Divine Sacrifice (Hebrews 1:1-3; Colossians 2:8-9; 2 Corinthians 5:19).
He purged our sins. None but God can do this (Isaiah 43:25).

5. Loving Sacrifice (Ephesians 5:25; Revelation 1:5).
The cross is the ultimate expression of God's love for sinful men.

6. Sufficient Sacrifice (1 John 2:2; Hebrews 10:14).
He fully and finally satisfied every claim of perfect justice.

The Finished Work

The Lord Jesus said to the Father, "I have finished the work which Thou gavest Me to do" (John 17:4). On the cross His final, exulting cry was "It is finished!" (John 19:30). What was the great work that He came to finish? "For the Son of Man is come to seek and to save that which was lost" (Luke 19:10). "The Father sent the Son to be the Savior of the world" (1 John 4:14). His mission was to "save His people from their sins" (Matthew 1:21). Consider how fully He completed the work which He came to accomplish.

1. He met the full demands of the Law against us (Romans 8:3-4).

2. He justified us from all things from which we could not be justified by the Law of Moses (Acts 13:39).

3. He freed us from all condemnation (Romans 8:1).

4. His own righteousness and holiness were satisfied (Psalm 85:10).

5. His work is sufficient to save all sinners (1 John 2:2; John 1:29; 12:32). But he cannot do so unless they come to Him (Matthew 23:37).

6. He "offered *one* sacrifice for sins forever" (Hebrews 10:12). No one should dare suggest the slightest addition to His finished work on the cross. It is the sole and sufficient basis for putting away our sins.

The Proof of Acceptance

The consistent proclamation of the early church was that God had raised Jesus from the dead. On this basis, men were called to believe upon Him (Acts 2:24, 32; 3:15, 26; 10:40).

1. He rose according to the Scriptures (1 Corinthians 15:4). He fulfilled a thousand-year old prophecy by doing so (Psalm 16:10; Acts 13:35-37).

2. He rose according to His own words (Matthew 12:39-40; 16:21; Luke 18:31-33). He specified the exact day of His resurrection (Matthew 27:63).

3. He rose in spite of a Roman guard watching over His tomb. Every effort was made to prevent a mere pretended resurrection (Matthew 27:63-66). He was seen by many witnesses (1 Corinthians 15:5-8).

4. He rose by the power of God and convincingly proved that all He said and did was fully accepted by God (Romans 1:3-4; Ephesians 1:19-20).

5. He rose because His resurrection is essential to our justification (Romans 4:25).

The greatness of this work does not change the necessity of man's response. All men are not automatically or universally saved. They must respond to Jesus Christ and His claims (John 3:18; Acts 3:19).

THE MEANING OF THE CROSS   **LESSON 8**

Millions say they believe that Jesus died on the cross for the sins of man, but they do not understand it. Prayerfully consider your understanding of this great truth by answering the following:

1. Jesus died on the cross because (select one)
    a. He was a victim of circumstance.
    b. He was a victim of a tragic mistake.
    c. sin must be judged if we are to be brought to God.
    d. He could not escape from either the Romans or Jewish leaders.

2. God is able to free sinners from the penalty of death by (select one)
    a. allowing them to do penance.
    b. overlooking their failures due to His love.
    c. providing a perfect sacrifice for sins.
    d. doing whatever He pleases because He is God.

3. If Jesus had not died on the cross we would have been (select one)
    a. hopelessly and forever lost.
    b. taught an equally acceptable way to God.
    c. forced to work harder to please God.
    d. accepted on the ground of His love.

4. Paraphrase (rewrite in your own words) 1 Peter 3:18 *or* Isaiah 53:4-5.

5. If God loved His Son, why did He allow Him to suffer and die at the cross (Romans 4:25; 5:6-8)?

6. For whom did Jesus die (John 3:16; I John 2:2)?

7. What did Jesus mean when He said, "It is finished" (John 19:30)?

8. Name one convincing proof of the resurrection of Jesus Christ.

9. *What do you say?* Explain in your own words why Jesus died on the cross.

10. *What do others say?* Contact at least three people this week and ask them the following questions. You may wish to say something like the following:

> "I'm involved in a Bible Survey here in (name city). Could you help me by sharing your opinion on three important questions? (1) In your opinion what was the purpose of Jesus Christ dying on the cross? (2) Do you believe that Jesus arose from the grave and is alive today? (3) What effect should belief in the resurrection of Christ have on a person's life? Thank you so much for your help. Would you like for me to mail / e-mail you a copy of the survey results? Thank you."

Record their names and addresses on the 3x5 cards provided by the class leader. Record the answers on the back, indicating if survey results are desired. Then return the cards next class meeting. Results of the survey will be tabulated by the class leader and mailed to each person indicating an interest.

"EXCEPT A MAN BE BORN AGAIN, he cannot see the Kingdom of God" (John 3:3). It was to a believer in God, a devoutly religious attendee of the synagogue, a moral person who came to pay Him honor, that Jesus Christ uttered these solemn words. All that Nicodemus had was insufficient to prepare for his eternal meeting with God. Are you prepared to meet God?

What is Meant by Being Born Again?

To be born again is to be regenerated (given new life). When Jesus told Nicodemus that he needed to be reborn, He spoke not of physical birth but of spiritual birth (John 3:4-6). Jesus questioned why he did not understand this as a teacher of his people (John 3:10). The rebirth or regeneration of the nation of Israel was taught in the Old Testament (Ezekiel 36:26; 37:1-10). The future rebirth of creation from its sin-cursed state was also a well-known teaching (Matthew 19:28). Nicodemus had not understood that rebirth is a word to be applied to the individual when he becomes a member of the family of God.

Being born again is a personal event. It is a new life, a new family relationship, a new power within. The Bible says we enter the Kingdom of God as one passing from death to life (John 5:24). We pass from walking in darkness to walking in light (John 8:12). We pass from the kingdom of Satan to the Kingdom of God's dear Son (Colossians 1:13). We become a new creation (2 Corinthians 5:17). This new creation is in righteousness, holiness and truth (Ephesians 4:24).

Why Must the Natural Man be Born Again?

The "natural man" refers to one just as he is born and lives in the flesh before new life from God is given.

1. He is Corrupt (Genesis 8:21).
He has a deceitful heart (Jeremiah 17:9). Within his flesh dwells no good thing (Romans 7:18).

2. He is Dead in Sins (Ephesians 2:1).
By God's standard, there is no spiritual life.

3. He is Controlled by Satan (Ephesians 2:2).

4. He is an Enemy of God (Romans 5:10).
He has no hope and is without God in this world (Ephesians 2:12). Every child of God was at one time in this condition.

How Can a Person be Born Again?

1. Two Illustrations of New Birth.

A careful study of John 3 will not support the ideas that most people have about entering the Kingdom of God. Jesus did not mention good deeds, joining religious organizations or going through religious ceremonies. He gave two illustrations of the new birth:

a. The Wind (John 3:8). It is invisible, unpredictable in its workings and yet evident in its effects. The Source is God and not man. The New Birth has its source in God (John 1:13). It is sent from Him to invisibly and powerfully work in changing lives.

b. The Serpent of Brass (John 3:14-15; Numbers 21:6-9). When the people had sinned, God directed Moses to make a brazen serpent and put it upon a pole. All who believed the word of Moses and looked to the object of God's providing were delivered. Jesus said He, as the Son of Man, would be "lifted up" like that serpent on the pole to be the object of faith that would save. That "lifting up" clearly was to be on the cross (John 12:32-33). The New Birth occurs by looking to Jesus as the One crucified for our sins.

2. Two Major Factors in the New Birth.

a. The Word of God (1 Peter 1:23; James 1:18). We hear the Word of truth and believe it to be saved (Ephesians 1:13; Romans 10:17). It is the seed of salvation (Matthew 13:3-9; 18-23). The New Birth comes when we genuinely believe God's Word and obey it.

b. The Holy Spirit (Titus 3:5; John 3:5, 6, 8). He convicts men of sin (John 16:8-11) and leads them to Christ. The New Birth is a work of the Holy Spirit. It begins with conviction of sin and leads to a cleansed life, "the washing of regeneration."

It will be noted that nothing of the above has anything to do with water baptism. In fact, baptism is not mentioned. Water is used in the Bible as a symbol of the Spirit (John 7:38-39) and of the Word (Ephesians 5:26). Baptism has nothing in common with the illustrations used by Jesus of the wind and the serpent of brass. Baptism is a picture of salvation. It is very important, and it follows the new birth, but does not cause it (Acts 8:12-13; 37-38).

What Are the Results of the New Birth?

1. We have a new heart and a new spirit (Ezekiel 11:19).
2. We partake of the divine nature (2 Peter 1:4).
3. We are indwelt by the Spirit of God (Romans 8:9).
4. We are children in the family of God (1 John 3:1).
5. We have eternal life (1 John 5:11-12).
6. We love the Lord Jesus Christ (1 John 5:1).
7. We love others, especially Christians (1 John 3:14; 4:7).
8. We have a will to obey the Lord Jesus (1 John 2:3).
9. We do not practice sin (1 John 3:9).
10. We practice righteousness (1 John 2:29).

Have you known conviction of sin and turned to Jesus Christ for deliverance? Have you believed the Gospel of your salvation and trusted in Christ?

THE NEW BIRTH

LESSON 9

Jesus said that one cannot see the Kingdom of God unless that person has been born again. Understanding this is crucial. Please answer these questions thoughtfully.

1. Answer by circling True or False.
   a. One is born again by being baptized in water. (True or False)
   b. The two illustrations of the new birth given by Jesus are the sea and the serpent of brass. (True or False)
   c. "Born again" is a catch phrase to be applied mainly to a change in our religion. (True or False)

2. Nicodemus first came to Jesus as (select one)
   a. a believer in God.
   b. a moral person.
   c. a synagogue attendee.
   d. a person interested in Him.
   e. all of the above.

3. "Born again" means (select one)
   a. joining the church.
   b. changing your religion.
   c. a new life from God.
   d. a gradual spiritual transition.
   e. believing in God.

4. The natural man must be born again because (select one)
   a. he is corrupt.
   b. he is dead in sin.
   c. he is controlled by Satan.
   d. he is an enemy of God.
   e. all of the above.

5. Paraphrase (rewrite in your own words) John 1:12-13.

6. What is the role of the Word of God in the new birth (Matthew 13:3-9, 18-23; Romans 10:17; Ephesians 1:13; 1 Peter 1:23)?

7. What is the role of the Holy Spirit in the new birth (John 3:6-8; 16:7-11; Titus 3:5; Acts 2:37)?

8. What are some results of the new birth?

9. *What do you say?* Explain the "New Birth" in your own words.

10. *What do others say?* Contact at least three people this week and ask them the following questions. You may wish to say something like the following:

> "I'm involved in a Bible Survey here in (name city). Could you help me by sharing your opinion on three important questions? (1) Many people are using the expression "born again." What does this expression mean to you? (2) In your opinion, how does a person become a member of God's family? (3) Why do you think Jesus used this expression to describe what it means to become a Christian? Thank you so much for your help. Would you like for me to mail/e-mail you a copy of the survey results? Thank you."

Record their names and addresses on the 3x5 cards provided by the class leader. Record the answers on the back, indicating if survey results are desired. Then return the cards the next class meeting. Results of the survey will be tabulated by the class leader and mailed to each person indicating an interest.

"FOR BY GRACE ARE YE SAVED through faith; and that not of yourselves: it is the gift of God: not of works, lest any man should boast" (Ephesians 2:8-9). Salvation is by grace, which means that it is the undeserved favor of God. It is a gift, which means that it cannot be bought or earned. Here is a doctrine that is difficult for people of a religious mind to accept. Often it is accepted partially or in some way that denies its truth.

The Old Testament word for grace meant "to stoop in kindness to an inferior." This is a perfect description of God's action toward us. The New Testament word means "favor, free generosity, kindness to someone, or a gift." This indicates that salvation is not earned, deserved or bought, either in whole or in part. Salvation in Jesus Christ is "the gift of God" and permits no payment to the Giver.

False Ideas of Grace

The reason of man would tell him that certain actions help in gaining merit for salvation before God. Consider these statements by the Word of God about such ideas:

1. Works or Deeds As a Way to God.

"If by grace, then it is no more of works" (Romans 11:6). "Not by works of righteousness which we have done, but according to His mercy He saved us" (Titus 3:5). The righteousness of God is graciously granted by God "to him that worketh not" (Romans 4:5). The one who tries to earn favor for salvation through human works is seeking to make God his debtor (Romans 4:4).

2. Keeping the Ten Commandments.

"Therefore by the deeds of the law there shall no flesh be justified in His sight: for by the law is the knowledge of sin" (Romans 3:20). "Ye are not under the law, but under grace" (Romans 6:14). "You have been severed from Christ, you who are seeking to be justified by law; you have fallen from grace" (Galatians 5:4 NASB). The contrast is seen in John 1:17, "For the law was given by Moses, but grace and truth came by Jesus Christ."

There can be no ground of boasting about the privilege to be with God (Romans 3:27). There can be no "staircase to God" built upon human righteousness or religious acts. Men are not saved by giving up something, by bargaining with God or offering to supplement with our efforts what He has done. Salvation is not by works, not by law-keeping, not by religious ceremonies and not by seeking to make God our debtor. It is by grace, and grace alone.

Why Is Grace Necessary?

1. The Moral Condition of Man.

He is without strength to morally approach God (Romans 5:6). He is a sinner (Romans 3:9), an enemy of God (Colossians 1:21), and dead in sins (Ephesians 2:1). How then could he make a way for himself to God?

2. The Absolute Holiness of God.

Man could never reach God by his own efforts. God's very holiness is beyond even the best of men (Isaiah 6:3-5). God stoops to man in grace.

What Are the Effects of Grace?

1. We Are Saved by Grace (Romans 3:24; 4:16).

There are no human additives.

2. We Are Kept by Grace (John 10:28-29; 1 Peter 1:5; 5:10).

He holds us in His hand and keeps us by His power. We are not kept through the law (Galatians 3:2-3) or by other works. We are under grace, not law (Romans 6:14).

3. We Stand in Grace (Romans 5:2; 1 Peter 5:12).

God deals with us on this principle.

4. We Live by Grace (Hebrews 13:21; Philippians 2:13).

It is God that works in us to empower Christian living.

Warnings About Grace

None of this is to suggest either a license to sin or any downgrading of our calling to live in a godly manner.

1. We Do Not Sin That Grace May Abound (Romans 6:1).

2. We Do Not Turn the Grace of God Into an Excuse for Impurity (Jude 4).

Liberty is not an occasion for wickedness but rather for loving sacrifice (Galatians 5:13).

3. We Are Saved Unto Good Works (Ephesians 2:10; Titus 3:8).

We do not practice sin (1 John 3:9). We keep God's Word (1 John 2:3-5). But these are the *fruits* of salvation and not the means of earning God's favor. We live for God because we love the Lord Jesus (John 14:15, 21).

The unique Christian message is the Gospel of Grace (Acts 14:3; 20:24, 32). This Gospel proceeds from the God of all grace (1 Peter 5:10) who receives us at the throne of grace (Hebrews 4:16). This is an abiding principle of the character of God and the manner of His dealing with us. We should never approach Him with any idea of obligation on His part.

STUDY GUIDE

SALVATION BY GRACE   **LESSON 10**

The Christian faith is unique in emphasizing the truth of salvation by grace. Other systems of approach to God deny this truth in whole or in part. Be sure that you understand this doctrine by answering these questions.

1. Observing the Ten Commandments (select one)
   a. is essential for the Christian's salvation.
   b. is to be joined together with Christ's work on the cross.
   c. can now be totally disregarded.
   d. is the perfect standard required for attaining God's righteousness.
   e. is none of the above.

2. Check the *most* accurate. Grace is God
   a. reaching those undeserving of His favor.
   b. reaching those deserving of His favor.
   c. reaching those deserving of His judgment.

3. According to Scripture, all men are (select one)
   a. basically good.
   b. basically seeking God.
   c. basically corrupt.
   d. basically well-meaning, but weak.

4. God can save sinners by grace and still be holy because (select one)
   a. Christ took the sinner's place and suffered for us.
   b. God can do whatever He pleases, even if inconsistent.
   c. sin is not all that serious.
   d. that is His duty to His creatures.

5. Paraphrase (rewrite in your own words) Ephesians 2:8-9.

6. Contrast two things in each verse below:

1 Peter 5:5

Jude 4

Galatians 5:4

Romans 11:6

Romans 4:4

7. Which of these Bible statements reflects grace?
   a. "This do and thou shalt live."
   b. "Thou shalt love the Lord thy God."
   c. "We love Him because He first loved us."
   d. "The soul that sinneth, it shall die."

8. What false idea about grace is corrected by Jude 4 and 1 Peter 2:16?

9. *What do you say?* State in your own words what the grace of God means to you.

10. *What do others say?* Contact at least three people this week and ask them the following questions. You may wish to say something like the following:

    > "I'm involved in a Bible Survey here in (name city). Could you help me by sharing your opinion on three important questions? (1) What was the purpose of the Ten Commandments? (2) Do you ever use the expression 'grace' in everyday speech such as 'grace period'? (3) What do you think the Bible means when it says we are 'saved by grace'? Thank you so much for your help. Would you like for me to mail/e-mail you a copy of the survey results? Thank you."

    Record their names and addresses on the 3x5 cards provided by the class leader. Record the answers on the back, indicating if survey results are desired. Then return the cards next class meeting. Results of the survey will be tabulated by the class leader and mailed to each person indicating an interest.

The jailer at Philippi asked, "What must I do to be saved?" The apostle Paul answered, "Believe on the Lord Jesus Christ, and thou shalt be saved" (Acts 16:30-31). But what does it mean to believe on the Lord Jesus Christ?

Many people have strange ideas on this crucial subject. Here are some common, unbiblical examples: people say, "I believe"

1. Because they acknowledge that Jesus lived and died here on earth;
2. Because they admire the morals and ethics of Jesus;
3. Because they joined a religious group;
4. Because they pray to God;
5. Because they repeated a prayer, doctrinal statement or formula.

Is this believing in Christ the Bible way? Does this kind of belief change people's lives? Does it give solid assurance of going to heaven?

What is Faith?

What is it to believe on Christ? Biblical faith has been defined as including the ideas of trust, personal confidence, persuasion and reliance. We say, "I believe in that person." It is opposed to doubt. It is not being gullible or naive. Faith has the following elements:

1. Faith Has an Object.

Faith is *in* someone or something. For Christians, this someone is a Living Person, the Lord Jesus Christ (Acts 20:21). "This is the work of God, that ye believe on Him Whom He hath sent" (John 6:29). The Lord Jesus asked the blind man, "Dost thou believe on the Son of God?" (John 9:35). The thief on the cross, to enter Paradise, had only to believe on Jesus (Luke 23:42-43). This belief was the heart of the Gospel message (Acts 8:35-37; 1 John 5:13). It is not *how much*, but *in whom* we believe. Faith receives *Him* (John 1:12).

2. Faith Necessitates Content.

We must hear the Word of the Gospel and believe it (Acts 15:7). The Corinthians were saved when Paul preached the Gospel to them. That Gospel, which is "the full Gospel," is carefully defined in 1 Corinthians 15:1-4. Christ died for our sins, was buried and rose again, all according to the Scriptures. Trusting Christ comes after hearing the Gospel, called the Word of Truth (Ephesians 1:13). This Gospel is so precious and vital that any man or angel who alters it is under a curse (Galatians 1:6-9).

3. Faith Has a Basis.

That basis is the Word of God (1 Thessalonians 2:13; Romans 10:17). Christian faith has as its object what is called "the witness of God" in the Scriptures (1 John 5:9). Faith accepts God's truth (1 Thessalonians 2:13) and believes that God is true, though every man may be a liar (Romans 3:3-4). We are not "leaping into the dark," exercising blind faith, or trusting in our emotions. We believe and rely upon God's Word.

4. Faith Brings About Action.

We may have the idea that faith is merely a mental agreement with a certain statement, but that is not so. Notice the action words in the following: people came to Jesus, fell down before Him and obeyed His Word; He told a man to stretch forth his hand (Matthew 12:13); He told another to take up his bed (Matthew 9:6); He commanded another to wash in a certain pool of water (John 9:7). Repeatedly He called for action.

Abraham is the model of a man who believed God. When Genesis 12:1-4, Acts 7:2-3 and Hebrews 11:8 are compared, it will be seen that he heard God's Word and responded by leaving his home town without knowing where God would lead him. This believing response clearly demonstrated his faith.

The faith that saves is a faith that produces action. Saving faith has never been merely a passive, mental assent to historical facts. Any so-called "faith" which has not works is a "dead faith." When a person truly believes in Christ the result will be a life of good works. (See James 2:14-26 where saving faith and "dead faith" are contrasted.) Saving faith is more than "believing *that*" the facts about Christ and His death are true. We "believe *in/on*" the Son of God, being committed personally to Him.

Examples of Faith

The Scriptures are filled with examples of faith. The eleventh chapter of Hebrews has been called the "Honor Roll of Faith" because it lists some outstanding men and women who had faith. Review these and mark the actions taken in their steps of faith.

Two other examples may be cited. The first is the faith of the centurion in Matthew 8:5-10. The centurion believed that Christ could heal his servant by merely saying the word. The other is the faith of the woman of Canaan (Matthew 15:22-28). She pleaded that the Lord would deliver her daughter from demons. Her faith was humble and persistent.

How to Come to Christ

When we come to Christ, a number of things are involved:

1. The Spirit Has Convicted Us of Sin (John 16:8-11).
We acknowledge our sinnership to God (Luke 15:18; 18:13-14).

2. We Repent of Our Sins (Luke 13:3; Acts 3:19; 17:30; 20:21).
We desire to change by turning from our sins to Christ.

3. There is Knowledge of the Gospel.
We must believe it to be saved (Acts 15:7-9; 1 Corinthians 15:1-4). The heart of that message is the Lord Jesus Christ.

4. We Believe God's Word (Mark 4:20; John 5:24).

5. We Receive God's Son by Faith (John 1:12; 1 John 5:12-13) **and Become His Follower** (John 10:4-5, 27).

6. As a Result We Confess Him Before Others (Matthew 10:32; Luke 12:8; Romans 10:9).

Saving faith rests its whole weight upon the Lord Jesus Christ and His finished work. Faith is the instrument, the means, and the channel through which the grace of God flows. It is not the source of salvation, not an act of merit, not a moral excellence which makes one worthy. It is the empty hand that accepts what God freely offers. Vengeance is upon those who obey not the Gospel (2 Thessalonians 1:8).

Faith gives all the glory to God. It can be exercised by all classes of persons of varying ages, positions and intelligence. It is universally available. False faith may name the name of Christ and do mighty works, but the Lord will expose and reject imposters (Matthew 7:21-23; Luke 13:28), for these are tares among the wheat (Matthew 13:24-30). True faith will manifest a change of life (Hebrews 6:9-10). True believers obey the Word of God (1 John 2:4-5), love fellow believers (1 John 3:14), do good works (Ephesians 2:10), practice righteousness (1 John 3:7, 10; Ephesians 4:22-24) and do not *practice* sin (1 John 3:9-10; Galatians 5:19-21).

Have you believed on the Lord Jesus Christ?

BELIEVING ON JESUS CHRIST

LESSON 11

The most important issue in time or eternity for every human being is whether we will be forever with God or separated from Him. Carefully think through the following:

1. I can be *sure* I am saved because (select one)
   a. I prayed a prayer to ask Jesus to come into my heart.
   b. God has answered many of my prayers.
   c. I have given up my old way of life.
   d. I now read the Bible and attend church.
   e. none of these.

2. Saving faith is (select one)
   a. agreeing with what the Bible says.
   b. believing in God with all my heart.
   c. believing that spiritual or religious things are essential.
   d. believing that Jesus lived and died and was history's greatest person.
   e. none of the above.

3. Define saving faith in your own words.

4. What did the "good thief" believe (Luke 23:39-43)?

5. List the three basic points of the Gospel in 1 Corinthians 15:1-4 and place a check mark beside the one that was/is most difficult for you to believe.

   a.

   b.

   c.

6. Paraphrase (rewrite in your own words) 1 John 5:9.

Do you fully accept this witness? Explain.

7. What was the evidence of true faith in the woman of Canaan in Matthew 15:22-28? Would you take the same position before the Lord Jesus?

8. In what way have you personally known or acted upon the following verses?

    Luke 13:3

    Luke 18:13-14

    John 16:7-9

    Romans 10:9-10

    Ephesians 1:13

    Revelation 3:20

9. *What do you say?* In what areas do you still have questions about what it means to believe in Jesus?

    If you died today and stood before God, and He asked you, "Why should I let you into My heaven?" what would you say?

10. *What do others say?* Contact at least three people this week and ask them the following questions. You may wish to say something like the following:

    "I'm involved in a Bible Survey here in (name city). Could you help me by sharing your opinion on three important questions? (1) One often hears the expression 'believe in Jesus Christ.' Do you think to 'believe' in Christ means more than mental assent to certain facts about Him and His life? (2) What do you think real belief is? (3) Do you think it is possible for people to trust God about everyday matters and not trust Him for their eternal future? Thank you so much for your help. Would you like for me to mail/e-mail you a copy of the survey results? Thank you."

    Record their names and addresses on the 3x5 cards provided by the class leader. Record the answers on the back, indicating if survey results are desired. Then return the cards next class meeting. Results of the survey will be tabulated by the class leader and mailed to each person indicating an interest.

ASSURANCE OF SALVATION

It has often been said, "No man can know for sure that he is going to Heaven." This is usually backed up by several objections. It is said that things we do in life might cause us to lose our salvation. On what basis can we know for sure that we possess eternal life? This question must be answered by the statements of Holy Scripture.

Possibility of Assurance

"These things have I written unto you that believe on the name of the Son of God; that ye may know that ye have eternal life" (1 John 5:13). You will note that it does not say that you may feel—or hope—or think—or imagine. It says, "ye may *know* that ye have eternal life." Over 30 times in his first epistle John repeats the word "know" in some form. Consider these phrases: "know that we know Him" (2:3), "know that we have passed from death unto life" (3:14), "know that He abideth in us" (3:24), "know that we are of the truth" (3:19), "know . . . that we dwell in Him" (4:13).

It is certainly true that "not every one that saith unto Me, Lord, Lord, shall enter into the Kingdom of heaven" (Matthew 7:21). Moreover, some who profess to be believers and have associated themselves with Christians will be turned away by the Lord (Luke 13:25-27). "By their fruits ye shall know them," said the Savior (Matthew 7:20). Yet, if there has been true spiritual rebirth sealed by the Holy Spirit (Ephesians 1:13), and evidenced by a person's life (1 John 2:6), a believer can be confident of eternal life right now (2 Timothy 1:12; Romans 8:38-39).

Assurance is defined as "confidence" or a "state of certainty." *Assurance of salvation* is the confidence or state of certainty a Christian has about his own salvation (eternal life). The Scriptures clearly indicate that God wants the Christian to know that he is heaven-bound. Assurance of salvation is not merely human optimism or presumption. It is a fact based on adequate (divine) testimony that we are in a right relationship with God.

Three Witnesses for the Believer's Assurance

God has given the Christian three witnesses that testify to his relationship with God, and on which he should base his assurance:

1. The Word of God.

This is our strongest witness. Just as our salvation is based on belief in God's Word (Genesis 15:6; Romans 10:9-10), so also our assurance is based on His Word. He that believeth on the Son hath everlasting life (John 3:16,

36; 5:24). Our salvation is based on the *fact* that we have the Son of God, not that we have a certain *feeling* (1 John 5:12). Nowhere do the Scriptures speak of "feeling" saved. If we come to Jesus, we have His word that He will not cast us out (John 6:37).

2. Objective Tests of Reality.

Another important witness is the reality of a *changed life*. The thief on the cross had limited opportunity to stand for Christ, but he did publicly confess his faith and rebuke the other thief (Luke 23:40-43). Although there are believers who live a carnal (fleshly) life (1 Corinthians 3:1-4), of whom Lot is typical (2 Peter 2:7-8); that is not to say their lives show no evidence of spiritual life. Human failure has Scriptural provision (1 John 1:9; 2:1-2), but this is not a license to sin. The following are Scriptural tests of divine life in the individual:

a. Confessing Christ (Romans 10:9-10)
b. Good works (James 2:14-26; Ephesians 2:10)
c. Obedience to the Word (1 John 2:4-5; 5:2-3)
d. Not loving the world (1 John 2:15)
e. Practicing righteousness (1 John 3:7, 10)
f. Not practicing sin (1 John 3:9-10; Galatians 5:21)
g. Love for fellow-believers (1 John 3:14)
h. Affirming Christ's Deity (2 John 9)
i. Willingness to admit and confess sin as a believer (1 John 1:8-9)

3. Inward Witness.

A third witness is our own feelings. This witness is the weakest of the three because it is subjective and a person may deceive himself. Yet, taken with the other two, it is a significant witness. The following are subjective tests of reality of divine life:

a. Witness of the Spirit with our spirit (Romans 8:16)
b. No more consciousness of sin as an unpaid debt (Hebrews 10:2)
c. Distress when we sin (Psalm 32:3-5)
d. Our own way of life has changed (see objective tests); we sense a reality in prayer; we have a concern for the lost; we have a desire for the Word, etc.

Doubting Christians Versus Unsaved Professors

Although doubts concerning our salvation are serious (and even sinful), most Christians are plagued with such doubts at one time or another in their experience. The following guidelines may prove helpful for those who question their own salvation:

Doubting Christians:	Unsaved Professors:
1. Are concerned about their relationship to God (they raise questions).	1. Tend to be careless, even confident.

2. Often show repeated concern about their salvation.

2. Vigorously affirm their salvation in face of contrary evidence in their life. Are resistant and resentful at any questions in this area.

3. Identify with Christians, though they often feel their own unworthiness to be one of them.

3. Often criticize believers and the church—blame them for various things, often in harsh language.

4. Often question their salvation during mental, physical "lows"—problem times in their lives.

4. Show little or no recognition of need at these times.

Dealing with Doubts

1. Recognize Doubts.

You may have had questions similar to the following: "When I accepted Christ, nothing happened—I did not feel different." "I don't know whether I believed in the right way." "I don't have the witness of the Spirit." "I believe I have committed the unpardonable sin." "My life does not show I am a Christian. I have failed so miserably."

2. Examine Yourself.

The following questions may help pinpoint a person's true spiritual state: "Have you ever known conviction of sin during your life?" "On what are you basing your hopes of heaven?" "When and under what circumstances did you receive Christ?" A true believer has known conviction of sin and repentance and is basing his hope of salvation solely on Christ and His work. Generally, he will be able to recall a point where he made an unconditional commitment to Jesus Christ as Lord and Savior; if he does not know the time, he will at least know that the commitment has been made.

3. Confirm by Prayer.

Consider a prayer of commitment to Christ as Lord and Savior if there is doubt. Repeated praying in this way, however, is no substitute for coming to the point of believing God's Word and resting upon it, rather than relying on feelings.

The Value of Self-Evaluation

Jesus warned against self-deception in regard to salvation. Many will claim to have known Him and to have done much in service for Him, yet they will be cast into outer darkness because they were not true believers (Matthew 7:21-23; Luke 13:23-28). Therefore, if we should have any doubts, we should examine ourselves whether we be in the faith (2 Corinthians 13:5) using the objective tests of reality given above. Commitment to Christ as Lord and Savior can be made if there are still doubts.

ASSURANCE OF SALVATION

LESSON 12

The next best thing to knowing God is having an assurance that we are His forever. How can we know for sure that we have eternal life? Carefully consider the following questions:

1. Which of the following statements best reflects the Biblical concept of assurance of salvation?
   a. I think I have eternal life.
   b. I hope I have eternal life.
   c. I know I have eternal life.
   d. I'll find out when I die if I have eternal life.

2. Answer by circling True or False.
   a. It is impossible for a person to know for sure he has eternal life. (True or False)
   b. It is possible to have assurance based on false reasons. (True or False)
   c. Some who say they believe will be lost. (True or False)
   d. Assurance of salvation is merely human optimism and presumption. (True or False)

3. Paraphrase (rewrite in your own words) 1 John 5:10-13.

4. What do the following verses indicate about a person's ability to know he has eternal life?

   1 John 2:3

   1 John 3:14

   1 John 3:19

   1 John 3:24

   1 John 4:13

5. Which of the following are the best witnesses of the reality of our relationship with God? List in order of importance from most reliable to least reliable.

   a.   Witness of friends

   b.   Word of God

   c.   Objective test of reality

   d.   Inward witness

6. From Matthew 7:21-23, why is it important that our assurance of salvation be based on sure grounds?

7. Which of the objective tests of reality listed in the chapter are true of your life?

8. Have you ever had doubts about your eternal destiny since receiving Christ as Lord and Savior? How did you deal with them?

9. *What do you say?* If someone were to ask you, "How do you know for sure you have eternal life?" what would you say?

10. *What do others say?* Contact at least three people this week and ask them the following questions. You may wish to say something like the following:

> "I'm involved in a Bible Survey here in (name city). Could you help me by sharing your opinion on three important questions? (1) Do you think it is possible for a person to know for sure that he has eternal life? (2) What do you think the Apostle John meant when he wrote, "These things have I written that ye may know that ye have eternal life?" (1 John 5:13) (3) Have you ever come to a place in your own spiritual experience where you knew for certain that you have eternal life? Thank you so much for your help. Would you like for me to mail/e-mail you a copy of the survey results? Thank you."

Record their names and addresses on the 3x5 cards provided by the class leader. Record the answers on the back, indicating if the survey results are desired. Then return the cards next class meeting. Results of the survey will be tabulated by the class leader and mailed to each person indicating an interest.

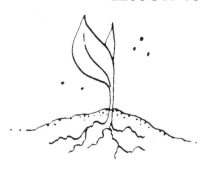

"I AM COME THAT THEY MIGHT HAVE LIFE, and that they might have it more abundantly" (John 10:10b). "He who believes in Me, as the Scripture said, 'From his innermost being shall flow rivers of living water.'" (John 7:38 NASB). "Whatsoever is born of God overcometh the world" (1 John 5:4). These tremendous claims for the life of the one who believes in the Lord Jesus are presented in a most forthright manner in the New Testament as the norm for Christian living. Peace, rest and spiritual power are not to be exceptional among the followers of our Savior, but rather the standard experience.

The Lord not only offers pardon for the guilt of sin and the assurance of life eternal, but also offers a new life in which the Spirit of Christ is working actively to transform our walk and to renew our minds. We can have that kind of life if we take heed to what the Scripture says about how it is to be lived. Spiritual blessing and power are not automatic for believers. They are highly conditional.

Words for the New Believer

We have reviewed the necessity of being sure that we possess eternal life through Jesus Christ our Lord. It is important to fix our hopes on clear promises in the Word of God concerning Him. It is also important to manifest a changed life as evidence of the reality of our claim to know the Lord Jesus. Here are some initial encouragements:

1. Confess Christ As Your Lord Before Others (Romans 10:9-10; Luke 12:8).

Refuse to be a silent, undercover believer.

2. Discontinue Harmful Habits and Associations (Psalm 1; 2 Corinthians 6:14-18).

Do not let others pull you down while you are trying to help them.

3. Seek a Mature Prayer Partner and Helper (Ecclesiastes 4:9-10).

There is greater progress and encouragement with this assistance.

Spiritual Life Principles

Victorious Christian living is not simply for missionaries and exceptional disciples. It is Christ's will for all His people (2 Corinthians 2:14; Ephesians 4:13). The following considerations mark the path of triumph each day:

1. Submit to Jesus Christ As Lord Daily (Colossians 2:6; 2 Corinthians 8:5).

He cannot bless the one who refuses to bow the knee to His supremacy and love. We are His and not our own (1 Corinthians 6:19-20).

2. Yield Daily to Every Prompting of the Holy Spirit (Romans 6:13-19; 8:14).

We are not to grieve, quench or resist in any way Him who is our in-dweller and anointing (Romans 8:9; 1 John 2:27). We are to be continuously filled, or controlled, by the Spirit (Ephesians 5:18). A Spirit-filled believer walks worthy of God (Colossians 1:10).

3. Be Occupied With Christ Himself, Rather Than Self (Hebrews 12:2-3).

We are to focus our thoughts upon Him (Colossians 3:2). Our entire life is to be Christ-centered and not self-centered. Turning from self is a necessary part of our transformation.

4. Obey the Word of God (John 14:15, 21; 15:10; 1 John 3:24).

To obey God is better than all sacrifices (1 Samuel 15:22). How can we call Jesus "Lord" and not do the things He says? (Luke 6:46). Freedom of the Spirit is not to do as we please, but rather to do as He pleases. Obedience to the Word brings additional light (Hebrews 5:14). We must will to do God's will (John 7:17). We can expect to be tested in this area of our willingness (Genesis 22:1-18). We should never call obedience to the Word "legalism." Legalism is adding to God's requirements—whether relating to salvation or living the Christian life.

5. Believe God and Trust Him for Every Need (Hebrews 11:8; John 14:1).

Our walk must be by faith (2 Corinthians 5:7). Faith is in one sense a gift of God but in another sense the moral responsibility of man. That is why Jesus rebuked some of His disciples for their unbelief (Matthew 8:26; Luke 24:25).

6. Serve Others for Jesus' Sake (Galatians 5:13; 2 Corinthians 4:5; Colossians 3:23-24).

He that watereth shall be watered (Proverbs 11:25). No believer can grow by simply absorbing blessings and giving out nothing. The famous illustration puts it: "The Dead Sea is dead because it is always taking in and never putting out."

7. Discipline Your Life (1 Corinthians 9:27).

Self-control, or temperance, is one of the fruits of the Spirit (Galatians 5:23; 2 Peter 1:6). The believer is told to "mortify" (put to death) the deeds of the flesh (Romans 8:13; Colossians 3:5). God works with us in this discipline (Hebrews 12:6-7).

The daily presentation of our body to God is necessary (Romans 12:1-2). We are to resist the devil (James 4:7), endure and overcome temptation (James 1:12), be zealous of good works (Titus 2:14) and love others (John 13:34). When we do wrong we are to confess and forsake the sin (Proverbs 28:13).

Provision-for-Failure Principles

Do believers ever stumble or fail? Of course they do. Consider David, Peter or others of God's greatest men. However, it is important to seek restoration to God lest we come under His discipline and correction (Hebrews 12:5-9). These are the divine remedies:

1. Fulfill Your Responsibilities.

a. Confess and forsake all thoughts or actions which you know to be outside the will of God (Proverbs 28:13; 1 John 1:9).

b. Make things right with others wherever possible (Matthew 5:23-24; Romans 12:18).

c. Be forgiving (Matthew 6:14-15; 18:35). Be forbearing (Colossians 3:13). Cover with love as much as possible (1 Peter 4:8; 1 Corinthians 13:4-7).

d. Get back into full fellowship with God in the Word and prayer and with other believers in the local fellowship.

2. Rely on Christ's Victory.

Break repeated cycles of failure and confession involving the same areas. Remember that the Lord Jesus has accomplished the basis for present deliverance from the power of sin in our lives.

a. He broke the power of the sin nature (Romans 6:6) and condemned sin in the flesh (Romans 8:3). We who were once the slaves of sin (Romans 6:20) have now been made free. This does not mean that this nature has been removed or eradicated (Galatians 5:16-17; Romans 7:21, 23; Matthew 26:41) but its former prevailing power has been annulled.

b. Believers no longer need to fear Satan. He was defeated at the cross (John 12:31; 16:11), and his power over believers was broken (Colossians 2:15; Hebrews 2:14). However, we are told to resist him (1 Peter 5:8-9; James 4:7), and we are not to give him opportunity (Ephesians 4:27).

c. The world includes a Satanic system of values, morals and ungodly influence that is the Christian's enemy (1 John 2:15-16). This differs from the world's inhabitants whom God loves. The system has been condemned by our Lord (John 12:31; 1 Corinthians 11:32). He prays for us to be kept from it (John 17:15). We have overcome it (1 John 4:4; 5:4).

Devotional Principles

Each believer must spend time daily with God. Our life is an intimate fellowship with the Person of the Lord. Certain practices characterize the believer whose life is being used and blessed of God.

1. Quiet Time.

The ear of the disciple is wakened to hear the voice of God (Isaiah 50:4). The first part of each day should begin with Him (Mark 1:35). Evenings and other periods may be set aside for Scripture study and prayers, but the experience of many of the saints in Scripture, as well as the example of our Lord Jesus, confirms the necessity of beginning the day with God. This regular time is for meditation and direct contact with God.

2. Prayer.

Our Savior said, "Men ought always to pray" (Luke 18:1). It was not an option in His earthly life and should not be an option for us. It should be our lifeline of communication with God. If we are not receiving, it is likely that we are not praying (Matthew 7:7). An important beginning for each day is to commit our bodies to the Lord for His purposes and to beseech His guidance through the day.

3. Study of the Word.

The Scriptures are given by God to be food for our souls (Hebrews 5:12-14; Psalm 19:10). We are to eat God's Word (Jeremiah 15:16). How can a young believer cleanse his way? "By taking heed thereto according to thy word" (Psalm 119:9). There is a place for meditative study of a short portion in the morning; systematic study, such as reading through the Bible; and special study for assignments. It is important to be able to read the Bible for ourselves and to make good personal applications of the truth. Memorizing Scripture is encouraged (Psalm 119:11).

4. Witnessing Overflow.

We are given power by God to be the witnesses for Jesus Christ in this world (Acts 1:8). The natural way of witness is to share our faith as a way of life with those around us. By overcoming the fear of man, we will be able to speak up for Christ before those around us who are lost and bound for a Christless eternity.

Church Principles

The Lord Jesus Christ has a great love for His church, in spite of all its earthly deficiencies (Ephesians 5:25). His church is made up of redeemed people. He wants them to gather together in various localities to encourage one another, worship the Lord, preach His word and obey His commands. The Bible does not contemplate a believer who is detached from the local church and fellowshipping with God on his own. A great passage on this subject is Acts 2:41-42. In studying this passage you will note normal church activities and responsibilities:

1. Baptism.

This is the public confession of the Lord Jesus Christ by new believers (Acts 8:36-37).

2. Apostles' Teaching.

The teaching of these men is now contained for us in the Bible, together with that of the prophets of the Old Testament, which is also the Word of God.

The preaching and teaching of the Word of God to companies of believers is one of God's appointed means for growth. It provides systematic instruction to supplement as well as to give direction and encouragement to personal Bible study.

3. Fellowship.

Believers are told not to forsake the assembling of themselves together with other believers (Hebrews 10:25). Those who forsake these companies are said to be "not of us" (1 John 2:19). Isolationism or individualism has no place in a healthy Christian experience. Note how the early believers stuck together (Acts 2:44-47). Notice the way most letters of the New Testament are addressed.

4. Breaking of Bread.

This has to do with the memorial feast of bread and wine instituted by the Lord the night in which He was betrayed (Luke 22:19-20). It was observed by the early believers (Acts 20:7; 1 Corinthians 11:23-34).

5. Prayers.

There is a place for joint prayers with other believers as well as individual prayer (Acts 1:14). There is an added value to joint prayer (Matthew 18:19). Mighty events came about as believers prayed together.

You may have given yourself to Christ as Lord and Savior. If so, that is the proper beginning. You must now commit yourself to Him that He might live His life in you day by day (Galatians 2:20). Thus He will be victorious in you and through you.

LIVING THE NEW LIFE

LESSON 13

Being "born again" is just the beginning of the new life of the believer. Many privileges and responsibilities are involved. It is important to understand the concepts below.

1. Jesus Christ came to give the believer (select one)
   a. eternal life.
   b. abundant living in this life.
   c. victory over the world and its temptations.
   d. all of the above.

2. When a person becomes a believer in Christ, it is important that he (select three)
   a. change his personality.
   b. confess Christ publicly to others.
   c. discontinue harmful habits and associations.
   d. seek help from a mature Christian.

3. Paraphrase (rewrite in your own words) 1 Corinthians 6:19-20.

   How does this passage affect you personally?

4. Identify the keys to victorious Christian living in the verses below:

   a. John 14:21

   b. Romans 12:1-2

   c. 2 Corinthians 4:5

   d. Ephesians 5:18

   e. Colossians 3:2

   f. Hebrews 11:6

5. Answer by circling True or False.
   a. It is possible to sin after becoming a Christian. (True or False)
   b. We have to sin. (True or False)
   c. It does not make any difference if we sin or not since "once saved, always saved." (True or False)
   d. We do not have to confess our sins after we are saved because God has already forgiven all our sins—past, present and future. (True or False)

6. What is God's part and man's part in forgiveness and restoration of the Christian (1 John 1:9)?

7. What actions are indicated in the following verses that will deepen our devotion and intimate fellowship with the Lord?

   Mark 1:35

   Psalm 119:9-11

   Acts 1:8

8. What five things were the believers in the early church actively engaged in (Acts 2:41-42)?

   Which of these have become a real part of your Christian life?

9. *What do you say?* What were the events leading up to the time that you became a Christian? What have been the most meaningful changes in your life since you were born again?

10. *What do others say?* Contact at least three people this week and ask them the following questions. You may wish to say something like the following:

    "I'm involved in a Bible Survey here in (name city). Could you help me by sharing your opinion on three important questions? (1) In your opinion, which is most important to a Christian: going to heaven or having a fulfilled life here on earth? (2) How would you describe the way a real Christian should live? (3) Do you feel it is important for a Christian to be actively involved in a local church? Why or why not? Thank you so much for your help. Would you like for me to mail/e-mail you a copy of the survey results? Thank you."

    Record their names and addresses on the 3x5 cards provided by the class leader. Record the answers on the back, indicating if the survey results are desired. Then return the cards next class meeting. Results of the survey will be tabulated by the class leader and mailed to each person indicating an interest.

1. Regeneration.

This is the new birth, the beginning of spiritual life for every believer (John 3:3-8). When divine life is imparted, the Holy Spirit enters the believer's body. This miracle is achieved through the hearing and believing of God's Word (Romans 10:17; Ephesians 1:13; 1 Peter 1:23), by the working of the Holy Spirit (John 3:5-6; Titus 3:5) and by our response to God of believing the truth (2 Thessalonians 2:13).

2. Reconciliation.

This is the bringing together of those who have been separated (2 Corinthians 5:18-20). One has pointed out that the idea of reconciliation in this verse is that of gaining the pardon of an offended king.

3. Redemption.

This means to deliver by paying a price (Romans 3:24; Hebrews 9:12). Believers were once the slaves of sin and uncleanness (Romans 6:17-20), the curse of the Law's terrible judgment (Galatians 3:13; 4:5), fear of impending death (Hebrews 2:15) and Satan's power (Colossians 1:13; 2:15; Hebrews 2:14-15). Now we have been made free in Christ (John 8:36) because He has paid the price with His own precious blood (1 Peter 1:18-19).

4. Atonement.

This refers to all that the Lord Jesus accomplished on the cross as the ground of salvation. Atonement is for all who will come to God (2 Corinthians 5:14-15; 1 Timothy 2:5-6; Hebrews 2:9). The Old Testament word meant primarily "to cover" but also indicated that sacrificial work by which God found full satisfaction in meeting the claims of His justice because of our sin. The Jewish Day of Atonement (Leviticus 16:33-34), today called Yom Kippur, is an example of the Old Testament use of the word. Romans 5:11 uses "atonement" in the King James Version, but there it should be translated "reconciliation." Hebrews 2:17 could be rendered "make atonement." A similar word, "expiation," is used in RSV and other translations of this verse. (See also "propitiation.")

5. Justification.

This is a Divine act whereby a holy God pronounces the sinner who believes in Christ to be righteous before Him and acquits him from all charges, apart from any merit of his own. This is done "freely" by His grace (Romans 3:24). It is to be noted that this is a declaration of God, not an experiential thing (Romans 4:4-5; 5:1; Galatians 2:16; 3:11). Justification is by grace, by faith and by His blood, without works and apart from the Law. Justification by works, referred to by James (2:14-24), is a demonstration of the reality of faith already possessed. This is not a justification unto salvation but an outward display of faith by action following salvation.

6. Imputation.

This means "to reckon" or "to put to one's account" by a judicial act of God. It is illustrated in Philemon 18. God put our sins upon Christ at the cross and He put Christ's righteousness upon us as believers (2 Corinthians 5:19, 21).

7. Mediator.

A middle man is needed to bring together a holy God and sinful men. This is the "daysman" for which Job longed (9:33) and which Christ proved to be (1 Timothy 2:5; Hebrews 8:6; 9:15; 12:24).

8. Propitiation.

The word is related to "mercy" or "mercy-seat," which was the place where the sacrificial blood was sprinkled before God in the Old Testament sanctuary (Romans 3:24-25; Hebrews 9:5-7; 1 John 4:10). Through Christ's work, not that of man, God has become favorable to us and the claims of justice have been satisfied. The man who prayed the sinner's prayer cried, "'God, be propitious to me'" (Luke 18:13 NASB, marginal reading).

9. Sanctification.

This has been described as that relationship into which men enter by faith in Christ (Acts 26:18). "Sanctify" means "to set apart" (1) from the defiling and sinful elements of this life and (2) unto the sacred purposes of God. Positionally in Christ we have already forever been sanctified in Him (Acts 20:32; 1 Corinthians 6:11; Hebrews 10:10; Jude 1). This was even true of the sinful Corinthians (1 Corinthians 1:2; 5:1-2). All believers are sanctified by being *in Christ* and hence are called "saints," or "holy ones," by reason of that union with Him. There is, however, another use of the word in a *progressive* sense. The Holy Spirit continues a sanctifying work in believers' lives, and we should respond to these efforts to mold us into the image of God's dear Son (Romans 8:29). We are called to be *in practice* what we are *in position*.

If you are not a Christian, and if you do not know how to become one, but if you are interested in the subject, and if you would be willing to give it a fair hearing, then you will find the following pages of interest.

The Christian message is here presented as a series of questions and answers: questions such as you might possibly ask, and answers based directly on the Bible.

Well, then, where shall we start? We shall start with the subject that gave rise to the necessity of the Christian Gospel in the first place, that is, with the subject of:

Sin

What is sin?

Sin is lawlessness, that is, doing one's own will without restraint of God or man. It is missing the mark, or coming short of God's standard of perfection in thought, word or deed. It is the failure to do what one knows is right. Romans 3:23; James 4:17; 1 John 3:4.

Where did the first sin take place?

The first sin took place in heaven, when Lucifer, the chief of the angels, desired to take God's place. He was then cast out of heaven and became known as Satan. Isaiah 14:12-15.

How did sin enter the world?

Sin entered the world through Adam when he disobeyed God by eating of the forbidden fruit in the Garden of Eden. Genesis 3:1-13.

Why did God allow sin to enter?

God made man as a free, moral agent with the power to choose between good and evil. His desire was that His creatures should choose to love and worship Him voluntarily, and desire good rather than evil. But if a creature has the power to choose good, he must of necessity have the power to choose evil. Genesis 2:15-17.

What would have happened to Adam if he had not sinned?

He would have enjoyed long life in the Garden of Eden. Genesis 2:17.

What happened to Adam when he did sin?

1. He became spiritually dead toward God.
2. He became subject to physical suffering, sickness and death.
3. He lost his innocence, became unrighteous and unholy, guilty and lost, an enemy and an alien. Genesis 3:7; Ephesians 2:1-3.
4. If he died in his sin, he would suffer eternal doom.

How did Adam's sin affect his children?

His sinful nature was passed on to all his posterity . . . "As by one man sin entered into the world, and death by sin; and so death passed upon all men, for that all have sinned" Romans 5:12. (See also vv. 13-19.)

Do you mean that we are all born into the world sinners because of Adam's sin?

Yes! Adam could only beget children with his own nature, and that nature was sinful. All children have to be taught to do right, but they know how to do wrong without being taught. Psalm 51:5.

As an illustration of this principle, a metal jelly-mold gives its shape to all the gelatin desserts or salads that are made in it. If you should drop the metal pattern and it becomes dented, all the future gelatin molds will show the effects of the fall.

Well, does that seem fair that Adam's sinful nature should be passed down to all of us?

Adam acted as a representative of the human race. Since we are all created as free, moral agents, perhaps we would all eventually have done the same as Adam did anyway.

Is there not some good in all men?

It depends on whether you are looking at it from God's standpoint or man's. God can find no good in man that would help to earn him a place in heaven. As far as righteousness or fitness for heaven is concerned, God says there is none. Man is totally depraved. Isaiah 1:6.

What is meant by the expression "totally depraved"?

It means that sin has affected every part of a man's being, and that although he might not have committed every sin, he is capable of doing so. Jeremiah 17:9; Romans 3:10-18; Romans 7:18. In addition, it means that he is totally incapable of pleasing God, as far as salvation is concerned, Romans 8:8.

But will God find fault with a person who has not committed the terrible sins of murder, drunkenness, immorality and so forth?

God sees not only what a person has done but what he is in himself. What a man is, is a lot worse than anything he has ever done. A filthy thought-life, a hatred of some other person, a lustful look—these are terrible sins in God's sight. Matthew 5:27, 28; Mark 7:21-23; Romans 8:7, 8. They separate man from God. Isaiah 59:1, 2.

But are not some sinners worse than others?

Undoubtedly they are, but we must not compare ourselves with others. People who do that are not wise. We will not be judged in comparison with others but in the light of God's holiness and perfection. Romans 2:1-3; 2 Corinthians 10:12.

Will all sinners suffer the same punishment?

No! All who die in their sins will spend eternity in hell. However, there will be degrees of punishment, depending on the opportunities a man has had to be saved and the sins he has committed. Matthew 11:20-24.

What about the heathen who has never heard the Gospel?

God has revealed Himself to all mankind in creation as well as in conscience. If a heathen lived up to this knowledge, God would send him further light so that he might be saved. But the heathen has rejected the knowledge of the true God and has worshipped idols of wood and stone. Therefore, he is without excuse. Romans 1:20. Without Christ, the heathen is lost, and that is why Christian missionaries go into all the world with the Gospel.

How could you prove to me that I am a sinner?

If you have to answer "No" to any of the following questions, then you are a sinner. If you have never trusted Christ as your Lord and Savior, then you are lost and you need to be saved.

YOUR
ANSWER

1. Do you love God with all your heart, soul, strength and mind? _____
2. Do you love your neighbor as you love yourself? _____
3. Would you like your friends to know the most impure thought you have ever had? _____
4. Is your life as holy in the dark as in the light? _____
5. Is it as pure when you are alone as when you are with others? _____
6. Is it as clean when you are away from home as when you are at home? _____
7. Have you always performed all the good you knew you should do? _____
8. Can you honestly say, "I have never taken the Name of the Lord in vain?" _____
9. Have you an unbroken record of never having told a lie? _____
10. Are you as perfect as the Lord Jesus Christ? _____

The Necessity of Salvation

What is God's attitude toward sin?

Because God is absolutely holy, He cannot approve or excuse sin. Because He is absolutely just, He must punish sin wherever He finds it. He has decreed that "the wages of sin is death." Romans 6:23.

What is God's attitude toward the sinner?

God loves the creatures whom He has made. While He does not love sin, yet He does love the sinner. Romans 5:8.

What is God's desire with regard to all sinners?

God's desire for all is that they be saved. He does not want them to perish. 2 Peter 3:9.

What problem was raised by the entrance of sin into the world?

It raised the problem as to how God could save ungodly sinners and still be righteous in doing so. Romans 3:26.

Why was this a problem?

God's love desired the salvation of sinners. Ezekiel 33:11. Yet because of His holiness, He could not permit sinful creatures to enter His heaven. 1 Corinthians 6:9, 10. In fact, His justice demanded that all sinners must die as a result of their sins. Hebrews 9:27. The problem then was this: how could God's love be satisfied without violating His holiness and His justice?

What would have happened if God had done nothing?

All sinners would have perished in hell. Psalm 9:17.

Isn't God too good to send men to hell?

God is good but He is also righteous and holy. Not one of His attributes can triumph at the expense of another. His love can only be exercised in a righteous, holy way.

Would God have been right if He had done nothing?

Yes. Then we all would have received exactly what we deserved. But God's love impelled Him to action.

How could God solve this problem?

He could solve it only by finding a substitute to die in the place of the guilty sinner.

What requirements would such a substitute have to meet?

First of all, he would have to be a *man*; otherwise the substitution would not be a fair one.

Then he must be a *sinless man*. If he were not sinless, he would have to die for his own sins.

Thirdly, he must be God, since the Substitute must be able to put away an endless number of sins of an endless number of people.

Finally, he must be *willing* to die for sinners; otherwise Satan would charge God with unjustly making an innocent victim die unwillingly for guilty rebels.

Could such a substitute be found?

Yes, God found a Substitute Who met all these requirements in the Person of His only begotten Son, the Lord Jesus Christ. Isaiah 53:4, 5.

The Work of Christ

Was Jesus truly man?

Yes, He was born as a baby in a hotel stable in Bethlehem, grew up in Nazareth, and ended His ministry at Jerusalem.

Was He sinless?

Yes, He was born of the Virgin Mary and thus did not inherit Adam's sin. He knew no sin; He did no sin; there was no sin in Him. 2 Corinthians 5:21; 1 Peter 2:22; 1 John 3:5.

Is Jesus God?

Yes, Jesus is truly God just as He is truly man. John 1:1; 10:30; Colossians 2:9; Hebrews 1:8.

Was Jesus willing to die as a Substitute for sinners?

Yes, He expressed complete willingness to do His Father's will, even if it meant death. Psalm 40:7; John 10:17, 18.

Could we not have been saved by Jesus' sinless life?

No, our sins could never have been put away by His sinless life. John 12:24.

Why did He have to die?

Our sins deserved eternal death. He must bear the punishment in His body on the cross. 1 Peter 2:24.

Was there any special requirement in connection with the death of the Substitute?

Yes, His blood must be shed. 1 Peter 1:19.

Why was this necessary?

God had decreed that without the shedding of blood, there is no remission of sins. Hebrews 9:22.

What is the importance of the blood?

The blood is the life of the flesh. The shedding of Christ's blood indicated the giving of His life as a Substitute for sinners. Leviticus 17:11.

What actually happened on the Cross?

In the three hours of darkness, God caused all our sins to be placed on the Lord Jesus. He died the death which those sins deserved. Luke 23:44.

What did Jesus cry at the end of those three hours?

He cried, "It is finished!" John 19:30.

What did He mean by this?

He meant that the work of redemption had been completed, that everything necessary for the salvation of sinners had been provided. Hebrews 10:14.

What happened to Jesus after His death?

His body was buried in a tomb, but on the third day God raised Him from among the dead. Luke 24:1-7; John 19:42.

Why was this necessary?

God indicated His complete satisfaction with the work of His Son by raising Him from the dead. Romans 4:25.

Did Jesus rise from the dead in a literal body?

Yes, His body was a real body of flesh and bones. Luke 24:39.

Could men be saved apart from the resurrection?

No, the resurrection was absolutely necessary for the salvation of others. 1 Corinthians 15:14-19.

What happened after the resurrection?

Forty days later, the Savior went back into heaven where He was honored and glorified by God, the Father. Acts 1:9.

Then He sent the Holy Spirit back to the earth to announce the wonderful news that a way had been provided whereby guilty sinners might be saved. Acts 2:1-4.

The Way of Salvation

Since Christ has finished the work of redemption, then are not all men saved?

No, Christ's work is sufficient in its scope and power to save all men, but it is effective only for those who are willing to receive Him. This may be illustrated by an incident from American history.

In 1830 George Wilson was tried by a United States Court in Philadelphia for robbery and murder, and sentenced to be hanged. Andrew Jackson, President of the United States, pardoned him. But Wilson refused the pardon, and insisted that it was not a pardon unless he accepted it. The question was brought before the Supreme Court, and Chief Justice John Marshall wrote the following decision: "A pardon is a paper, the value of which depends upon its acceptance by the person implicated. It is hardly to be supposed that one under sentence of death would refuse to accept a pardon, but if it is refused, it is no pardon. George Wilson must hang." And he was hanged. (Lee, Roger G., The Sinner's Savior [Nashville: Broadman Press, 1950] pp. 35, 36.)

Why doesn't God save everyone?

He desires to do so. 1 Timothy 2:4.

However, He has chosen to give men their choice in the matter of salvation. Otherwise He would take men to heaven who didn't want to be there, and for such it would scarcely be heaven.

What must happen to a person before he can go to heaven?

His sins must be put away and he must be given a new nature that enables him to enjoy heaven. John 3:3, 5.

How is a person saved?

"By grace are ye saved through faith." Ephesians 2:8, 9.

What is meant by grace?

Grace is the unmerited favor of God shown to people who deserve the very opposite. It is God offering salvation to man as a free gift. Romans 5:8; Ephesians 2:7.

What is faith?

Faith is belief or trust. It is man receiving salvation from God as a free gift.

What must a person believe to be saved?

He must believe on the Lord Jesus Christ. John 3:16; John 20:30, 31.

Is it not enough to believe that there is a God?

No, even the devils believe that, and tremble, but they are not saved. James 2:19.

What does it mean to believe on Jesus?

It means to confess that you are a sinner needing salvation and to receive Him as your only hope of salvation, acknowledging Him to be Lord of your life. Romans 10:9.

Is it not sufficient to believe all the historical facts about Jesus?

No, a person may believe all that the Bible says about Jesus and still be lost.

What else is necessary then?

True belief involves a commitment of one's entire self to Jesus as only Lord and Savior.

Can a man have faith and not be saved?

Certainly! Faith in an unworthy object will only bring disappointment. Our faith must be in Christ if we are to be saved.

Can anyone do this?

Salvation is offered to all, but it is only those who admit themselves to be lost who will ever want to be saved. Luke 19:10.

Who produces this conviction of sin in a person's life?

The Holy Spirit of God is the One who produces conviction of sin. John 16:8-11.

What can a person do then, who does not realize he is a sinner?

He should read the Bible and be honest. Romans 10:17.

What will happen then?

He will see that he is a sinner and that if he dies in that condition he will go to hell. John 8:21, 24.

Will he be saved whenever he sees this?

No, he must then repent of his sins and receive the Lord Jesus Christ as His Savior. Proverbs 28:13; Act 16:31.

To be saved simply through faith seems to be too easy, doesn't it?

It might seem to be too easy, but it is God's only way of salvation. While it may seem easy to us, we should remember that it was a very costly transaction for God; it cost Him the death of His only begotten Son. So it is an easy salvation but not a cheap one. Isaiah 1:18.

Why did God decide that salvation should be given on the basis of faith?

The reason probably is that believing on Him is the only proper thing that all normal people can do. Even a child can believe.

But isn't there some work a person must DO in order to be saved?

No, there is no work a person can do. Christ finished the work on Calvary's cross. All the sinner has to do is believe. Titus 3:5.

Well, isn't that a contradiction? You say there is nothing to DO. All you have to DO is believe.

There is nothing you can *do* by way of earning or meriting God's approval. There is nothing you can *do* to buy your way or help purchase your admission to heaven. Romans 4:4, 5.

Faith is a non-meritorious act. A person cannot be proud because he believes in the Lord; what is more reasonable than for a man to trust his Creator? Thus, faith excludes human boasting, and is the only thing a person can do without doing a "good work" that he might think would entitle him to heaven. Romans 3:27.

You mean to say then that we are not saved by good works?

That is what the Bible says: ". . . not of works lest any man should boast." Ephesians 2:9.

Why couldn't man be saved by doing good works?

Man is a sinner and everything he does is stained by sin. The best he can do is like filthy rags in God's sight. Isaiah 64:6.

But suppose that I could live a perfect life from this day forward, would I not be saved?

No, you would not, because God requires that which is past. Your past sins must somehow be put away before you could enter God's presence. Ecclesiastes 3:15.

You mean to say, then, that decent, self-respecting, cultured people don't go to heaven?

The only people who go to heaven are those who acknowledge themselves to be sinners and who confess Jesus Christ as Lord and Savior. Matthew 21:31.

Are there not some people who are not good enough for heaven and not bad enough for hell?

No, there are only two classes of people, saved and unsaved. 1 Corinthians 1:18.

Well, then, are there not some people who are too wicked to be saved?

No, the Gospel invitation is extended to all mankind, and whosoever will may come. Isaiah 55:7; 1 Timothy 1:15; Hebrews 7:25.

Doesn't a person have to clean up his life before he can be saved?

As long as he thinks he can clean up his own life, he won't feel the need of the Savior. He should simply come to Christ just as he is, sins and all, and receive pardon and peace. Isaiah 1:18; Matthew 9:13; Luke 19:10.

Couldn't I be saved by following the example of Jesus?

Jesus' life was sinless. No mere man is able to follow that example. Moreover, the only reason Jesus died is because men could be saved in no other way. 1 Peter 2:24.

If believing on Jesus is the right way, then why do the vast majority of people refuse to accept Him!

Satan has blinded the minds of those who believe not, lest the light of the glorious gospel of Christ should shine unto them. 2 Corinthians 4:4. There is a way which seems right unto men, but the end thereof are the ways of death. Proverbs 14:12.

Couldn't a person be saved by trying to keep the Golden Rule?

No, when Jesus said, "Do unto others as you would have them do unto you," He was speaking to those who were already saved. He never intended it as the way to heaven.

Well, could we not be saved by obeying the Beatitudes or by living according to the Sermon on the Mount?

Once again, these teachings were addressed to those who had already acknowledged Jesus as Lord. To obey them requires Divine life, and a person receives this life when he is saved.

Surely, you aren't going to tell me that a person cannot be saved by keeping the Ten Commandments?

No one can fulfill what is demanded by the Ten Commandments. Romans 3:20.

Exactly what do the Ten Commandments require?

The Ten Commandments are as follows:
1. Thou shalt have no other god before me.
2. Thou shalt not make unto thee a graven image, etc.
3. Thou shalt not take the Name of the Lord, thy God, in vain.
4. Remember the Sabbath day to keep it holy.
5. Honor thy father and thy mother.
6. Thou shalt not kill.
7. Thou shalt not commit adultery.
8. Thou shalt not steal.
9. Thou shalt not bear false witness against thy neighbor.
10. Thou shalt not covet. (See Exodus 20:1-17.)

Were the Ten Commandments not given by God to His people?

Yes, they were, but He never intended that they should serve as a means of salvation. Galatians 2:16; 3:11.

Why then did God give the Commandments?

They were given to show the people what sinners they were. Just as a straight line shows up a crooked line, so the law shows men how far they have departed from God's standard of perfection. Romans 5:20; Galatians 3:19.

Has anyone ever kept these laws perfectly?

The Lord Jesus Christ is the only One who has ever kept the law perfectly.

Then are we not saved through His keeping of the law?

No, we are only saved through His death, burial and resurrection. We are condemned and cursed by the law. Galatians 2:21.

If a man could keep the law all his life, would he be saved by this?

Such a man would need to have been born a perfect being. But the Bible states: "If we say that we have not sinned, we make Him [God] a liar, and His word is not in us" 1 John 1:10.

Suppose that a man could keep nine of the Ten Commandments! Would he be saved?

No, the law demands continual and complete obedience. If a person breaks one commandment, he is guilty of all. James 2:10.

What is the punishment for failing to keep the law?

Death, now and forever. Galatians 3:10.

Weren't the Ten Commandments made for good people?

No! ". . . the law is not made for a righteous man, but for the lawless and disobedient, for the ungodly and for sinners, for unholy and profane, for murderers of fathers and murderers of mothers, for manslayers, for whoremongers, for them that defile themselves with mankind, for menstealers, for liars, for perjured persons, and if there be any other thing that is contrary to sound doctrine . . ." 1 Timothy 1:9, 10.

What effect should the Ten Commandments have on us?

They should make us realize what guilty sinners we are, and should cause us to cast ourselves on the mercy of the Lord. Romans 3:19.

But does it seem reasonable that we should be saved by faith alone and not by faith plus good works?

The Scripture says, "Not by works of righteousness which we have done, but according to His mercy He saved us . . ." Titus 3:5.

Does it say somewhere in the Bible that faith without works is dead?

Yes, it says that in James 2:20.

Doesn't that show that salvation is by faith plus works?

No, it does not. The teaching of the passage is that a man may *say* that he has faith but if he does not have good works, it shows that he was never truly saved. That kind of a faith never saved anyone.

What kind of a faith does save?

The kind that is not merely a matter of the lips but is a matter of the heart and which results in a new life filled with good works.

Then you mean that good works follow salvation, but do not secure it.

Yes, that is right. We are not saved *by* good works, but we are saved *unto* good works. Ephesians 2:8-10.

Is it not necessary to join some church in order to be saved?

Joining all the churches in town wouldn't save a person. "Ye must be born again."

But doesn't God expect us to join some church?

Whenever a person is saved he becomes a member of the true church composed of all true believers in the Lord Jesus. Then he should find fellowship in some local church where Christ is acknowledged as Head and where the Bible is accepted as the only inspired Word of God, our sufficient guide in all matters of faith and morals.

Does not the fact that I was baptized as an infant mean that I am saved?

Baptism is not the Savior. Only Jesus Christ can save. John 14:6.

But shouldn't people be baptized?

Those who have been born again should be baptized. There is no clear record in the New Testament of unsaved people or infants ever being baptized, however.

Then I am not saved by partaking of the communion service either?

No. Once again, the communion service was only intended for those who are already born again believers in the Lord Jesus Christ.

Do you mean to say that church attendance, gifts to charity, participation in the ordinances and similar observances will not help in my salvation?

They will not help at all. The only thing that will help you is to come to Christ as a sinner, repent of your sins and trust Him as your only Hope for heaven. Acts 4:12.

General Difficulties

How do I know that the Lord will accept me if I believe on Him?

He has said that He will, and He cannot lie. "Him that cometh unto me I will in no wise cast out." John 6:37.

But doesn't it seem like a leap in the dark—this business of believing?

No, it is the surest thing in the world. Banks may fail, businesses may go bankrupt, governments may topple and men may break their promises. But God cannot go back on His Word. He has promised to save all who accept Christ by faith. John 3:18.

Could I be saved if I am not one of the elect?

The Gospel isn't for the elect, but for all the world. God makes a genuine offer of salvation to any person in the world who will receive Christ Jesus as Lord. You can be saved if you will do what God says. John 3:36.

I would like to be saved but I am afraid I wouldn't be able to hold out.

No one has the strength in himself to hold out. However, when God saves you, He gives you strength you never had before. Every believer has the Holy Spirit of God living within him. It is from the Holy Spirit that the child of God receives power to live the Christian life. Romans 8:14.

Suppose I have committed the unpardonable sin?

The unpardonable sin, according to the Lord Jesus, was saying that the miracles He performed were done in the power of the devil. Have you ever said this? If not, then you have not committed the unpardonable sin. Matthew 12:31, 32. But if you die rejecting Christ, you will have committed an equally serious sin for which there is no forgiveness. Mark 8:36, 37.

But trusting Christ means that I will have to give up a lot, does it not?

Christ does not come to steal, kill or destroy, but to give life and to give it more abundantly. John 10:10.

An unsaved sailor once said to his Christian buddy, "I just can't face the cost of becoming a Christian." The buddy's reply was, "Have you ever faced the cost of *not* becoming a Christian?"

But there are so many hypocrites in the church.

Don't despise those who are real, just because some are hypocrites. Determine rather that you will be out and out for the Lord.

Sometimes I think I have believed in the Lord Jesus but have I believed in the right way?

If you have no other hope for heaven apart from Jesus Christ, if you have repented of your sins, if you made a complete commitment of yourself to Him, then you have believed in the right way.

Would it not be all right for me to postpone any decision about salvation until I am near the end of my life?

Four Scriptures answer this question.

1. "Boast not thyself of tomorrow; for thou knowest not what a day may bring forth." Proverbs 27:1.

2. "He that being often reproved hardeneth his neck shall suddenly be destroyed and that without remedy." Proverbs 29:1.

3. "Remember now thy Creator in the days of thy youth, while the evil days come not, nor the years draw nigh, when thou shalt say, I have no pleasure in them." Ecclesiastes 12:1.

4. "Behold, now is the accepted time; behold, now is the day of salvation." 2 Corinthians 6:2b.

Is there no other way I can come to God except through Jesus?

There is no other way. 1 Timothy 2:5, 6.

Relationship and Fellowship

Do Christians sin?

Yes, Christians sin every day in thought, word and in deed. They are guilty of sins of omission as well as sins of commission.

Should Christians sin?

No, God's will is that Christians should not sin. 1 John 2:1.

When a Christian sins, does he lose his salvation?

No, salvation is the free gift of God, and once it is given, it is never taken back again. Romans 6:23.

But doesn't the penalty of those sins have to be paid?

Jesus Christ bore the penalty of those sins when He died on the Cross of Calvary. God does not require the penalty to be paid twice.

You mean, then, that a Christian is still a child of God, even though he sins?

Yes, his relationship in the family of God is eternal. When a son is born into a human family, he will always be a son of his parents. He may subsequently disgrace them by his behavior, but he is still their son. So it is in the Divine family; relationship is established by the new birth and nothing can ever change it. John 1:12.

What does happen, then, when a Christian sins?

One thing that happens is that fellowship with the Lord is broken. 1 John 1:6.

What is fellowship?

Fellowship is the happy family spirit that results from all the members having the same interests, and sharing things in common. Consider the following illustration. A judge in the criminal court finds a robber guilty and sentences him to twelve months in jail. When the judge goes home that night, he finds that his little boy has been naughty. But does he sentence him to twelve months in jail? No, he no longer acts as a judge, but as a father in a family. The child is still his son, even though naughty. Because of sin, the happy family spirit has been broken and it remains broken until that sin has been confessed and forgiven. So the child is probably sent upstairs and he remains there until he is willing to confess his wrong. The great point is that relationship was not affected but fellowship was.

When a person is a sinner, God is his Judge. But when that person becomes saved, God is henceforth his Father.

Then you mean to say that once a person is saved he can never be lost?

That is what the Bible says. "They shall never perish." John 10:28. "Shall not come into condemnation, but is passed from death unto life." John 5:24; Romans 8:38, 39; 2 Timothy 1:12; 1 Peter 1:5; Jude 24, 25.

Cannot a person decide to be saved and later change his mind?

When a person has once committed his life to the Lord Jesus Christ, then his eternal salvation becomes the sole responsibility of the Savior. John 6:39. The Lord is honor-bound to take that person home to heaven. And because the Holy Spirit dwells in the true believer, he will never change his mind about being saved.

Does that mean that a Christian can sin all he wants and still be saved?

A true Christian will not want to sin, because he has a new nature that hates sin. 2 Corinthians 5:17.

But suppose a Christian goes on in willful and habitual sin?

If a person lives that kind of a life, it is certain proof that he was never truly born again. 1 John 3:9, 10.

Can a Christian sin and get away with it?

No, he cannot. While it is true that the *legal penalty* of his sins has been paid once for all at Calvary, it is also true that God administers *parental discipline* to his erring children. Galatians 6:7, 8.

How does God discipline his children?

Sometimes it is through sickness or adversity and in extreme cases through death itself. 1 Corinthians 11:30.

Does sin in a believer's life have any other consequences in this world?

Yes. He loses his joy. His prayers are hindered. His fruitfulness is marred. His guidance becomes obscure. He suffers shame and remorse. Opportunities are neglected and privileges forfeited. Finally, his testimony is ruined.

Does sin in a believer's life have any eternal consequences?

Yes, he suffers loss at the Judgment Seat of Christ. 1 Corinthians 3:15; 2 Corinthians 5:10.

Suppose that a Christian should die with unconfessed sin?

As mentioned previously, the penalty for all a believer's sin was borne by the Lord Jesus. When he died, all the Christian's sins were future. Since he paid the complete penalty, we can say He died for the believer's past, present and future sins.

Unconfessed sins, however, will result in a loss of reward at the Judgment Seat of Christ.

Is it possible for a Christian to backslide?

Yes, any child of God may wander away from the Lord.

How may we guard against backsliding?

By reading the Word of God, by spending time in prayer and by maintaining fellowship with the people of God.

What is the remedy for backsliding?

The cure for backsliding is confession and forsaking of sin, and, if possible, making restitution for wrongs which we have committed.

How To Know For Sure!

If I trust Christ as my Lord and Savior, what will happen inside me to tell me that I am saved?

If you mean some mysterious feeling or emotional experience, then it is quite probable that nothing like that will occur.

How then will I know that I am saved?

In a very simple way. God says He saves those who believe on the Lord Jesus. Whenever you believe on Him, you can know that you are saved because God says so. 1 John 5:10-12.

You mean to say that I may not feel it in my body?

That is correct. The real act of salvation takes place in heaven. That is where the fact is recorded. When God sees your faith, He justifies you.

But shouldn't a person feel different when he is saved?

Certainly, he should, but feelings are not the proof of his salvation. A person will not really feel happy until he knows he is saved. The order is this:

Salvation through faith in Christ.

Assurance through the promise of God.

Joy because of this assurance.

Then a person knows he is saved through the promises of God in the Bible?

That is the first and foremost way by which he knows he is saved. 1 John 5:13.

Would you say that feelings are not a dependable guide?

The trouble with feelings is that they are so changeable. One day a person may feel he is saved and the next he may not.

The Word of God never varies. How much better, then, to have our assurance of salvation based upon the Word of God.

Is the Bible the only way by which we can know we are saved?

No, there are several others.

1. A love for our fellow Christians. 1 John 3:14.
2. A new love for holiness. Romans 7:22.
3. A new hatred of sins. Romans 7:24.
4. A steadfast continuance in the faith. 1 John 2:19.
5. The witness of the indwelling Holy Spirit. Romans 8:14, 16.

May a person be saved and not know it?

It is possible that a person may really have been born again and yet not know it, either because of inadequate teaching or because of doubts placed in his mind by Satan.

May a person think he is saved and yet not be?

Certainly, many think they are saved because of their character or works, but they are not saved at all. Matthew 7:22, 23.

Is it necessary to know the day and hour of one's conversion?

No, it is not. Many people have such a distinct experience that they can tell the exact time and place. Others may not remember when they first trusted the Savior. The important thing is to be able to say, "I know I am saved right now because my faith and trust are in the Lord Jesus Christ alone."

Do most Christians have doubts about their salvation at one time or another?

Most Christians are probably subjected to Satanic doubts some time after their conversion.

What should one do when he is plagued with doubts?

The best thing to do is to quote Scripture to answer the doubts. When Satan insinuates that the believer is not saved, the latter should quote Gospel promises, such as John 5:24, which assure salvation to all who receive the Lord Jesus. Just as the Lord used the Word to repel the temptations of Satan in the wilderness, so we should use the Bible to drive away his doubting lies. Matthew 4:4, 7, 10.

If I am not sure whether I have ever really accepted Christ, what should I do?

You should get it settled right now by saying from your heart, "Lord, if I have never trusted Thee before, I here and now receive Thee as my only Lord and Savior."

Holiness

Doesn't a person have to live a holy life in order to become a Christian?

No, a sinner is not able to live a holy life until after he is saved.

Does God expect Christians to lead holy lives?

He most certainly does. 1 Thessalonians 4:3; Titus 2:11-13.

Does any Christian live a life of sinless perfection?

No Christian lives sinlessly. 1 John 1:8, 10. The Lord Jesus Christ is the only Person who ever lived a perfect life.

How is it that Christians can still sin after they are saved?

The reason is that the believer still has the old, evil, corrupt nature with which he was born. This is not removed at the time of conversion. Romans 7:17.

In what way, then, is the believer different from the unsaved?

The believer has a new nature which he receives at conversion. Scripture speaks of this as "the divine nature." 2 Peter 1:4.

What is the difference between these two natures?

The old nature is incurably bad and continually seeks to drag the Christian down into sin. Romans 7:21.

The new nature is only capable of good and seeks to lead the believer in paths of holiness. Romans 7:22.

Why did God allow the evil nature to remain after conversion?

The old nature teaches us our own nothingness and weakness and makes us continually dependent on the Lord for strength to resist temptation. Romans 7:24.

Are all Christians tempted?

Yes, all Christians are tempted. 1 Corinthians 10:13.

Does a Christian ever have to yield to temptation?

No, a Christian only sins when he wants to. He has the power of the Holy Spirit living within him, and this power is sufficient to deliver from all temptation. Galatians 5:17.

What is God's attitude toward the old nature?

God saw that it was worthy of death, so He condemned it at the Cross of Calvary. He does not try to reform it, improve it or clean it up. It is utterly hopeless and so God sees it as having been put to death when Christ died. Romans 6:6.

What should be the believer's attitude toward the old nature?

He should keep it in the place of death; that is, whenever the old nature tries to tell the Christian what to do, he should refuse to obey that which has been condemned by God. Romans 6:11, 12.

What should be the believer's attitude toward the new nature?

He should feed it, cultivate it and encourage it through study of the Scriptures, spending time in worship and prayer, serving the Lord and otherwise doing those things that are pleasing to the Lord. Galatians 5:22, 23.

What, in brief, is the secret of living a holy life?

The secret is in being occupied with the Lord Jesus in worship. We become like what we worship. There is no once-for-all way of achieving holiness; it is a life-long process. 2 Corinthians 3:18.

Can you give any other practical helps toward holy living?
1. Guard your thought life. You can control what you think. Philippians 4:8.
2. Make no provision for the flesh. Romans 13:14.
3. Remember that Christ lives within your body. Colossians 1:27.
4. In moments of temptation, cry to the Lord to deliver you. Matthew 14:30.
5. Keep busy for the Lord. Ecclesiastes 9:10.
6. Engage in some physical exercise. 1 Timothy 4:8.

But doesn't the Christian have to keep the Ten Commandments in order to live a holy life?
The Scripture teaches that the believer is not under the Ten Commandments as a rule of life. Romans 6:14.
1. The purpose of the law is to make men realize they are sinners and not to make them holy.
2. The law condemns to death all who do not keep it perfectly. No one can be under the law without being under this curse.
3. Christ paid the penalty of the law which we had broken, and now the law has nothing more to say to the child of God. Romans 10:4; Galatians 3:13.

Does that mean that the Christian can go out and commit murder and adultery?
Not at all. The Christian doesn't want to do these things because of his new life. Men under law live in fear of punishment. Men under grace are constrained by love to Christ. Love is a much stronger motive than fear. Men will do for love what they would never do because of fear.

If the Ten Commandments are not the believer's rule of life, what is?
The life and teachings of Jesus are the pattern and guide for the Christian. 1 John 2:6.

In what way are the teachings of Jesus different from the law?
This is answered in the fifth chapter of Matthew. The law said, "Thou shalt not commit adultery." Jesus said, "Whoever looks on a woman to lust after her hath committed adultery with her already in his heart." See verses 27, 28.
The law said, "An eye for an eye and a tooth for a tooth." Jesus said, "Resist not evil, but whosoever shall smite thee on thy right cheek, turn to him the other also." See verses 38-42.
The law said, "Love your neighbor and hate your enemy." Jesus said, "Love your enemies." See verses 43, 44.

Is it possible for men to live as Jesus taught?
Humanly it is impossible. But the Lord has given the Holy Spirit to all believers so that they will have the power to live in this supernatural way. 1 Corinthians 6:19; Galatians 5:16,17.

Standing and State

If believers still sin, how can God ever take them to heaven?
All who believe on Christ are given a perfect standing before God, even if their state may be far from perfect. Colossians 2:10.

What is meant by a believer's standing?
It means the position of complete favor he has with God because He is in Christ. Romans 5:1, 2.
The Christian has no right or merit in himself to stand before God. His only title to heaven lies in the Person and Work of the Lord Jesus. Thus God accepts us, not because of who or what we are, but because we belong to Christ. Ephesians 1:6.

How can God look upon unrighteous people as righteous?

He can do it because Christ bore the punishment of their sins in His body on the Cross. Ephesians 2:13.

Does it teach this in the Bible?

Yes, it distinctly says this in 2 Corinthians 5:21: "For He (God) hath made Him (Christ) to be sin for us, Who knew no sin, that we might be made the righteousness of God in HIM."

Do I understand, then, that God accepts all believers because they come to Him in the Person of His Son?

Yes, that is right. Christ is man's only title to heaven.

"I stand upon His merit,
I know no other stand,
Not e'en where glory dwelleth,
In Immanuel's Land."

How long does a believer enjoy this perfect standing before God?

He enjoys it as long as Christ enjoys it, because he is in Christ, accepted in the Beloved One. Ephesians 1:13, 14.

What is meant by the believer's state?

This means his everyday spiritual condition here on earth. Just as his standing is what he is in Christ, so his state is what he is in himself.

Is the believer's state sinless?

No, the believer's state is oftentimes far from being what it should be. Colossians 3:8, 9.

What is God's will concerning the believer's state?

God's will is that his state should grow more and more like his standing. This is a process that should be taking place continually throughout the Christian life. Colossians 3:1.

Will a believer's state ever correspond exactly to his standing?

Yes, when Christ takes him home to heaven his condition will be as perfect as his position. 1 John 3:2.

Why should a Christian want to have his state correspond increasingly with his standing?

His love for Christ should make him desire this. John 14:15.

After Salvation—What?

What is the first thing a person should do after he has trusted Christ?

Common courtesy would suggest that he thank the Lord for saving his soul. Luke 17:14-19.

Is it necessary to confess Christ to others?

Confession is not necessary to obtain salvation, but it is certainly necessary for growth in the Christian life. No one can ever expect to advance in the things of God who is ashamed of his Savior. Matthew 10:32, 33; Romans 10:9, 10; 1 Peter 3:15.

How does a person go about confessing Christ?

It is simply a matter of telling others what great things the Lord has done for you. Mark 5:19.

How long should a new convert wait until he is baptized?

Obedience should be prompt. Baptism is a lovely opportunity to publicly identify oneself with Christ in His death, burial and resurrection. By this act we are saying that we deserved to die but that Christ died for us. Therefore, when He died, we really died, because He died in our place. We witness that we likewise were buried with Him, and that we rose with Him to walk in newness of life. Romans 6:3-10.

Does baptism give us merit before God as far as our salvation is concerned?

No, baptism is an act of obedience to the teaching of the Lord Jesus. Those believers who die without being baptized will be unbaptized for all eternity.

How should a young convert know which church to join?

First of all, he should realize that he became a member of the true church, the Body of Christ, whenever he was saved. 1 Corinthians 12:13.

In addition, he should seek to identify himself with some local church where Christ is acknowledged as Head, where the Bible is accepted as the only guide, where the two ordinances of the church (baptism and the Lord's Supper) are observed, where a good teaching ministry is carried on, and where the Gospel is faithfully proclaimed.

In associating with Christians, he should feel a deep sense of responsibility to contribute to the welfare of the fellowship by loving service, fervent prayer and sacrificial giving.

What do you consider the most important things which a Christian should do each day?

Spend time in the Word of God and in prayer each day, and confess and forsake sin whenever it is allowed into one's life. Psalm 119:9, 11.

Discipleship

What does the Lord expect of one who is saved?

He expects a total commitment of that person to Himself. He expects the person to go where He leads, to do what He says, to be what He wants him to be. He expects him to forsake all he has, take up the cross and follow Christ. Romans 12:1, 2.

Is it reasonable that God should expect this?

Yes, it is the only reasonable response that a person can make to the Lord.

Doesn't a person have to think about himself?

Our chief responsibility in life is to please God. If we seek the Kingdom of God and His righteousness, He will see that we have some means of livelihood. Matthew 6:33.

Does that mean that I may have to go to the mission field?

It may mean that and it may not. But it does mean that you should be willing to go. Luke 9:23-26.

But I see so many Christians who are enjoying the comforts and luxuries of the world, and who do not seem to be all-out for Christ.

You must not compare yourself with other Christians. Your example is the Lord Jesus, and you must follow His steps. Luke 14:25-35.

Does Christ really expect us to "hate" our relatives?

He expects our love for Him to be so great that all other loves are hatred by comparison. Luke 14:26.

Can I not acknowledge Jesus as my Savior and not as my Lord?

Scripture gives no encouragement to such an attitude. If the Lord Jesus is not worth everything, He is not worth anything.

Then salvation involves a complete surrender to Christ?

That is exactly right. Nothing short of this will do.

God's Answers to Man's Questions is a booklet by William MacDonald, published by ECS Ministries © 1958, 2006, 2012 William MacDonald. All rights reserved.

The life and ministry of Jesus Christ clearly shows the purpose for which He came into this world—to bring sinful men back to God. The practical application of that great truth for a person who has never trusted Jesus Christ as Savior and Lord is to receive Him into his or her life.

The following is a simple Gospel presentation, useful for Christians to share with others. It also shows the way to Jesus Christ, whose life and ministry you have just studied, if you have never received Him as your own Savior and Lord.

The Bible teaches that God loves all men and wants them to know Him.

But man is separated from God and His love.
"God is on one side and all the people on the other side." *1 Timothy 2:5, Living Bible*

Why is man separated from God and His love?

Because he has sinned against God.
"Your iniquities have made a separation between you and your God." *Isaiah 59:2*
"For all have sinned and fall short of the glory of God." *Romans 3:23*

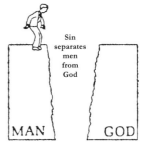

Where does this separation lead?

This separation leads only to death and certain judgment.
Man is "destined to die once, and after that to face judgment." *Hebrews 9:27*
"Those who do not know God . . . will be punished with everlasting destruction and shut out from the presence of the Lord." *2 Thessalonians 1:8-9*

<u>But</u>, there is a solution.

Jesus Christ, who died on the cross for our sins, is the way to God.
"God is on one side and all the people on the other side, and Christ Jesus Himself man, is between them to bring them together, by giving His life for all mankind." *1 Timothy 2:5, Living Bible*
"Christ died for your sins once for all . . . to bring you to God." *1 Peter 3:18*

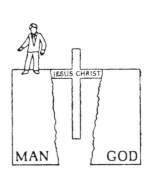

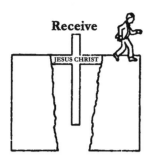
Receive

Does this include everyone?

No. Only those who personally receive Jesus Christ into their lives, trusting Him to forgive their sins.
"Yet to all who received Him, to those who believed in His name, He gave the right to become children of God." *John 1:12*

Each one must decide for himself whether to receive Christ.

Jesus says, "Here I am! I stand at the door and knock. If anyone hears My voice and opens the door, I will go in and eat with him, and he with Me." *Revelation 3:20*

How does a person receive Jesus Christ?

Jesus said, "You may ask Me for anything in My name, and I will do it." *John 14:14*

Therefore if you pray sincerely, asking Him—
Lord Jesus, please come into my life
and be my Savior and Lord
Please forgive my sins,
And give me the gift of eternal life
     —He will do it now.

If you have invited Jesus Christ into your life, the Bible says you now have eternal life.

"And this is the testimony: God has given us eternal life, and this life is in His Son. He who has the Son has life; he who does not have the Son of God does not have life." *1 John 5:11-12*

Notes

Notes

Notes

Notes

Notes

Notes